GO AHEAD — KILL YOURSELF!

SAVE YOUR FAMILY THE TROUBLE

Paradoxical Therapy with Families

Tom M. Saunders, Ph.D.

Family Systems Consultants
The Chrysalis Foundation, Inc.

dp

DISTINCTIVE PUBLISHING CORPORATION

Distinctive Publishing Corporation
P.O. Box 17868
Plantation, FL 33318-7868
Copyright 1990 by Tom M. Saunders, Ph.D.
All rights reserved.

All names used in illustrations are hypothetical and the stories generic. The family dynamics in each situation illustrated are accurately portrayed.

Produced by Ratzlaff & Associates
Cover design by Tom M. Saunders
Cover art by Christian Mildh
Cover production by Therese Cabell
Printed in the United States of America.

Library of Congress Cataloging in Publication Data
Saunders, Tom M. (Thomas Minor), 1942-
      Go ahead — kill yourself! : save your family the trouble : paradoxical therapy with families / by Tom M. Saunders.
        p.   cm.
      Includes bibliographical references and index.
      ISBN 0-942963-06-7 : $14.95
      1. Family--Mental health.   2. Family--Psychology.   3. Family psychotherapy--Popular works.   4. RedII : Nothing about Paradoxical therapy per se TMT.   I. Title.
RC455.4.F3S28   1990
616.89'156--dc20
                            90-44102
                            CIP

For Dietra and Lisa

CONTENTS

Tom M. Saunders, Ph.D.

INTRODUCTION

OK, OK — so the Introduction doesn't come before the Preface. But then what therapists in their right minds would offer to kill a suicidal person?

"I'm *not* suicidal!" screamed the angry young anorectic woman in defense. "I just don't like eating — and what's wrong with that?"

"I don't see anything wrong with that either. There will just be more to go around for those who wish to stay fat. In fact, it may be in your best interest to lose a few more pounds so that your family will take planning your funeral seriously."

"You make me furious . . . I can't believe that people come to you for help!"

"That's probably true. Your dad has been sitting here for twenty minutes and hasn't said a word. Maybe he prefers that you not compete with Mom anyway. After all, if you leave home, he's not going to have much left to live for himself."

And so the paradox goes — staying in balance — governed by the same laws of Nature that keep the solar system intact.

The strength of the paradox is in the Yin/Yang complementary role of each of the opposing sides. As A increases in strength, B decreases, and vice versa. The adolescent who demands freedom is begging for structure. The thrill of shoplifting without being seen is in constant tension with wanting to be caught. The threat of self-destruction always has contained, at its core, the frustrated desire to live life more fully.

By joining forces with the resistance, therapists leave the resistor no place to turn but to defend the opposing side, and therein, begin to have a choice about what it is they are not wanting to choose.

Paradoxical therapy, by definition, is confusing, disorienting, and anything but logical. The most immediate response from participants is anger that the therapists are being absurd or ridiculing — yet, the therapists are only mirroring the process presented by the family itself.

This book, much like the therapy which it describes, is presented in a similar fashion. Take each chapter for itself, in and of itself. Don't try to make connections or look for a theme or outline. If, in fact, there is one, it may become apparent weeks later — maybe months — maybe never!

Enjoy and become a part of, if you dare, without trying to understand.

PREFACE

These notes to myself about families are to help remind me of lessons already learned. Lessons that are dear should not have to be repeated so often. Not so, I find. The piper has often been paid with borrowed funds.

These notes may be useless to anyone else; they are my personal lessons.

These notes are mine.

Don't search for continuity or outline — there is none apparent.

When you find yourself confused, try to stay with it; you won't understand my lessons, but out of the confusion, you will learn some important lessons of your own.

My Mother has always told me that I can't have my cake and eat it, too. Why would I want a cake that couldn't be eaten? Is there a cake so beautiful that one need only look and not taste? She didn't know — couldn't answer — said that I would understand when I grew up. I still don't understand at 48! What a relief it is not to have to grow up.

And then there is patience: another virtue that supposedly comes with age. I still want it NOW!! But breaking warm bread and cutting hot pie were considered sins where I grew up. Better to wait for it to cool; it will look better that way. Who the hell cares how a hot pie looks or how far it runs? Pies are for taste — not to be blue-ribboned at a county fair, then thrown out because they are stale, yet beautiful.

So my decision to publish at an early age is a selfish

one — while I am still hot and runny.

These notes are not for blue ribbons. They have been learned at great expense. As you read, they are already changing.

There is little documentation, only where material has been directly plagiarized. Most of the ideas have been indirectly borrowed. A few border on being original.

Sand remains sand while piling in different dunes. $E = mc^2$. " . . . and there is no thing new under the sun."

TMS

DEDICATION

This book is a gift to all of the electric people in my life. You have kept my battery topped, restored my charge when I was empty, and brought me back on line when I became disconnected.

I first discovered electricity much like Franklin. Three years old at the time, I had just rebuilt an abandoned electric iron belonging to my grandmother. As always, there were parts remaining.

Grasping the plug firmly with my index finger between the prongs, I learned first hand about being charged and how blowing a fuse can save a life.

The second time, at ten, it was a radio that caught my fancy. This time, I learned about grounding. By placing my arm on a "live" metal radio chassis while standing on a damp garage floor, I discovered that a hot spark makes absolutely no difference in my life until it finds a path to the Earth.

Perhaps the most important lesson came at the county fair — the bumper cars — those wily, turn-on-a-dime miniature autos that connect to an electric net above by a rounded pole extending from the rear of the car.

The fun continued as long as the pole touched the net and the "gas" pedal was held to the floor. But when jarred off course and disconnected, the vehicle became a useless metal shell. Waiting by the side of the arena for someone to lift it back into position, the shell's only value was as scrap metal until once again connected to the source.

When the last quantum physicist has died trying to explain such simple facts about electricity, the Energy which lights our souls will still Be. Many useless shells will have come and gone, but the electricity of the Spirit will remain.

You are the Spirit who lights up my life!

FOREWORD

White light, through a prism, becomes a rainbow of infinite shades.

Hands, on a clock face, move through each second of perceived time as geared wheels turn, one against the other.

The knee bone, disconnected from the hip bone, is without meaning.

In each system, the sum of the parts is always greater than the whole.

As each gear wheel in the clock moves, it drives the gear wheels next to it in the opposite direction. Those gears, in turn, pass their energy on to their neighboring gears by turning them in the *same* direction as the original.

Small gear wheels move faster to keep movement in balance with larger gear wheels which move slower.

And so, with family systems, each person experiencing change is enmeshed with the energy of every other gear wheel in the system.

Change is healthy. Change is necessary. Change always involves dying and being reborn.

In the confusion of these transitions, the family can harness its energy and become stronger, or can stay fearful of the unknown and become fragmented.

The choice is always ours.

"Please kill me, Lord; I'd rather be dead than alive [when nothing that I told them happens]."

Then the Lord said, "Is it right to be angry about this?"

Jonah 4:3-4
The Book

1

ADDING INSULT TO INJURY: THE DON RICKLES APPROACH TO THERAPY

"You've got to be kidding! First, you want me to tell my fifteen-year-old son that he has to come to therapy — then you want me to ask him to pay part of the fee from the money that he earns? He doesn't even have a job. Can I pay him to wash the car?"

Shades of comedian Don Rickles. This modality of therapy would turn Tough Love converts into fainthearts. There can only be one possible motive: therapists who just want to have fun!

Asking for the impossible is a way of life for the therapist who wants to maintain integrity as well as sanity. Unfortunately, most of our training as helping professionals is geared toward learning to sacrifice our lives in the name of saving others. Addressing this lifestyle in its accelerated form, there is only one word that best describes the process; that is —

Suicide!

An old joke that has traveled the circuit for years asks, "How many psychologists does it take to change a light bulb?"

The answer: "Only one . . . but the light bulb has to want to change." The expressed desire of persons to want change in their lives is often a complete contradiction to what they do which poses a clear resistance to change.

Therapists are often seduced to believe what people say instead of watching what they do. In so doing, therapists often embark on a *Mission Impossible* where not only the tapes self-destruct, but the therapists do as well.

The myth of Sisyphus comes to mind as a visual metaphor for most therapy. Every day of his life, through eternity, Sisyphus was condemned to push a large boulder up the side of a mountain. By sundown, he would always near the top — only to let go of the boulder, and to start at the bottom again the next day. What appears as an apparent gain as the boulder is pushed near the top of the incline is often lost by the next session because an individual has time in between to return to the security and familiarity of old habits.

When therapists themselves are content with listening to such sagas, they are only a mirror of the persons they ostensibly seek to help. Such awareness signals the need to examine the therapists' own resistance and to not perpetuate the myth that resistance belongs to the people with whom they work.

Margie, for example. Margie has been seeing a social worker in a mental health outpatient clinic twice a week since she left the hospital two months ago. Hospitalized for depression, she is also being seen for three minutes each week by a participating psychiatrist who refills her prescriptions, including a healthy dose of anti-depressants.

Known best for her placid temperament, Margie rarely displays anger except when the social worker approaches the subject of suicide and timidly suggests that perhaps the accidental overdose of twenty anti-depressants that brought her to the hospital could be a hint of suicide.

Married to a dominating, overbearing husband for more than twenty years, Margie insists that she could not even think of killing herself because her husband could not make it without her. While it's true that her children needed her, the last of three is just out the door to make it on his own.

Responses on *The Life Changes Scale* (See Appendix A) indicate the loss of two close friends within the past year — a male, her only close male confidant, in an auto accident, and a female, her age, to cancer.

Margie reports that the children have avoided her because she is no fun to be with anymore, and her husband has shown no interest in her at all since they stopped having sex several years ago.

While few would argue that Margie should be depressed, to say nothing of angry, nowhere in her treatment plan does it suggest that her family should accompany her to the clinic. Her chart reveals that her depression has to do with a chemical imbalance as a justification for her drug prescriptions.

The focus here is not on Margie, but on the social worker for whom Margie is one of twenty individuals with similar profiles that the social worker sees in any given day. The clinic, appropriately called The Crisis Center in the community, is so understaffed that these twenty emergencies constitute only one fourth of the social worker's case load.

So who is suicidal?

Resistors

In the world of electricity, a resistor is a small coil of wire baked in a ceramic capsule that is put in line to impede current flow. By serving as a floodgate, like a dam in the river, the resistor controls the flow of electricity. Simultaneously, the resistor must temporarily absorb the resulting build-up of internalized heat which must then be dissipated through its ceramic shell.

What better visual image could there be of a therapist's role who is willing, usually for pay (though sometimes not) to listen for hours to persons wanting only to talk about all of the people in their lives to whom they cannot talk — all of whom are not in the room to even commence a possible dialogue. However, to begin inviting those significant others to participate in the process can only happen when the therapist is open to believing that it can happen.

The "Impossible" Request

There is an old cliche in the medical profession that individuals are diagnosed as alcoholics only when they drink more than their doctors do. A similar axiom is found in the life insurance profession where a salesman will rarely offer to write more coverage than he carries on his own life.

For therapists to consider expanding the therapeutic process to include all of the so-called "resistant members" of a person's extended family, they must be willing to relinquish control of the session as well as responsibility for the outcome. Since therapists, by their very nature, are people willing to accept either active or passive responsibility for the life of another, this first task of "letting go" is often the most difficult.

Secondly, therapists must have put to reasonable rest the communication issues with their own family members. This rule, simply put, is like promising never to pray the Lord's prayer (asking that forgiveness be granted us in the same manner that we forgive) until we have, in fact, done our own forgiving. Without finishing our own forgiveness first, our prayers could be answered in a most adverse way.

The next "impossible" task is to treat any form of resistance (from the persons making the excuses) as their unwillingness to face the risk of responsibility for their own lives. This single issue, bottom line, is the only issue ever being negotiated in therapy. There is no gray area in responsibility any more than one can be a wee bit pregnant.

With these decisions having been put in place, the therapists may have reduced personal impedance to a minimum and can now begin offering playful resistance of another kind.

From Insult to Injury

As Don Rickles so often demonstrates, humor is a wonderful tool for reducing the Goliaths in our life down to sling shot size. The first telephone interview might go something like this:

"Can you help me? My wife made me call you. She says I need help and that you are said to be one of the best."

"I don't think that I can help you . . . I'm already married."

"She says that I'm a workaholic, and that I'm never there when she needs me . . . but then she is always preoccupied with the kids when I do get home."

"Did your father also die at an early age?"

"Wait a minute . . . this doesn't have anything to do with my father . . . and how did you know that anyway?"

"Just a lucky guess. Are your kids angry with you, too?"

"I don't think so, but my wife almost called you last month. She found out that our fifteen-year-old son was sneaking out his bedroom window at two in the morning to spend time with his girlfriend."

"Are you bringing your girlfriend with you to this session?"

(Very long pause accompanied by beads of sweat.) "I didn't say anything about having an affair . . ."

"Apparently you haven't talked with your son lately. By the way, she will need to meet with your family as well."

"Oh, my God . . . she would never do that. Her husband doesn't even know."

"Well, he would have to be there, too, then . . . no use in playing ball with only half of the team."

(Beginning to sound a little terse.) "Look . . . I didn't call for an appointment with the neighborhood. I just need to learn how to please my wife . . . and frankly, I don't think that's possible."

"Then you had probably better call your mom and ask her to come with you. Might as well find out why you didn't make it with her."

(Gasp — exasperated.) "There's no way we can do

that . . . she would die if she found out that I were having an affair."

"Seems like everyone has to die sometime. Besides that, she didn't die when she found out about your father so I would imagine she'll make it through this one. What about your wife's parents anyway?"

"My wife's father died in a car accident when she was 16. Her mother has been an emotional basket case ever since, and she is living with us now because she is ill and can't take care of herself anymore . . . it's worse than having a baby to care for . . ."

"Perhaps we'll need to meet in your home to make it easy for her. By the way, you'll need to let them all know that they must share a part of the fee . . . we don't want anybody to think that they are doing someone else a favor."

"That's not fair. My wife's mother is ill and isn't even working . . . and my mother is on social security."

"It sounds as if you need to discuss this with them and call me back — either when you're ready to be honest or the situation has become stressful enough for you to be willing to change. Let me hear from you soon. Goodbye."

Assume that the affect in the therapist's voice speaking above is of a loving and nurturing nature. Those individuals calling have already sensed this or they would never have revealed so much of themselves.

Also, the art of reading between the lines is derived from trusting in the sixth sense and being willing to follow your heart instead of your mind.

Children, for example, seem to be the best graphic example of how the family "balance" is maintained through what has been inappropriately called "dysfunction." Until all members of a family decide that the current state of functional balance is not healthy for them, the craziness depicted in the example above will continue to be functional in spite of a covey of therapists.

For those who have not experienced throwing themselves in front of such a bulldozer with everything to lose, including their lives, a word from the wise should suffice. Contrary to lip service or platitudes about what a family would like to have happen, if they are not willing to confront each other with love, then they are not ready to be involved intimately with anyone.

Functional Dysfunction

This state of impaired homeostatic balance in a family system might best be called *functional dysfunction*. One of its hallmarks is that the system becomes tenaciously more rigid when faced with confrontation or intervention by well-meaning therapists.

The Stonehedge family is a case in point. Grandfather William, also known as the chauvinistic patriarch, has struggled with his daughter, Rebecca, since long before the onset of puberty. As there were no apparent male heirs to the throne and his daughter clearly could not understand business matters, the family business, a small manufacturing firm, would remain in the hands of the patriarch until his grandson, Bill, came of age.

However, diagnosed by a psychiatrist as paranoid schizophrenic at age thirteen, Bill has clearly abdicated his eldest son position to his older sister, Lila. Being a new generation woman and the apple of Grandfather's eye, Lila seemed to be the designated heir by default.

On his deathbed, Grandfather willed his business and substantial financial holdings to his granddaughter, Lila, in a skip-generation trust. As Lila was 22 at the time, she was also named as Trustee, thus, padlocking the family fortune just out of reach of his own daughter, Rebecca.

Worse yet, the newly established legal command made it impossible for Rebecca to acquire any financial resources without first groveling before her daughter with whom the tension was extremely aggravated.

Bill had never heard of schizophrenia. His problems began long before conception when his errant father threatened divorce if his wife became pregnant. Being true to his threat, Dad left home shortly after his wife's second pregnancy — Bill.

Determined to be a super parent, in spite of, Rebecca has compulsively logged a mental diary of Bill's every move (or non-move) since his first kick in her womb. Lila had used this time, wisely, to become more self-reliant.

Enter, the therapist. Not having yet learned that such tense situations call for a team approach (much more like the Noah's Ark approach to balance) the therapist becomes engaged with the "hurting" person in the family, the schizophrenic son, just recently released from the hospital without the benefit of follow-up.

Through such conscientious, painstaking effort, the therapist, a single psychiatrist in her mid-thirties, has been successful in establishing a bridge with Bill, paid for by Bill's trust. The bridge is wobbly, at best, shored up with medications and a strong desire on the therapist's part to reach Bill. Yet the closer that she seems to be in reaching Bill, the more their relationship is undermined by his well-meaning mother.

Not an unusual situation, Bill and his mother have become a very tight marriage, without any of the benefits, from the same time period in which his parents began to disconnect. Any attempts, conscious or unconscious, by the therapist with what appears to be dissolution, will cause a countermovement on the part of Bill and his mother, who will then become more tightly bonded.

By focusing on this "marriage" between Bill and his mother within the context of their entire extended family, a co-therapy team might side with the "team" and thus overload the circuits.

"It looks to me like Bill and you get along far better than his dad and you ever did."

"Well, it's true. Bill has always been an easy child . . . never belligerent. He sometimes tries to please me too much."

"That's certainly good news. I've never heard a woman complain before that her mate was doing too much for her."

"That's about the third time that you've made the mistake of making it sound like Bill and I were married . . . I think that's kind of sick on your part."

"Mate is actually ship talk for a hierarchy of command — who leads and who follows — long as everyone is in agreement, and you can work out who's on the top and who's on the bottom."

In anger, Mother is beginning to defend what she isn't doing and how she isn't doing it. She will probably leave angry and confused, and report the same to others. There is always a possibility that she won't come back, and will find another therapist who is easier to seduce with her point of view. What becomes blatantly clear in the process is that any movement on Bill's part, toward a healthier way of life, will threaten the end of the emotionally incestuous relationship with her son, and leave her, faced for the first time, with making it on her own. Facing up to her own major changes that lie ahead requires a fully conscious effort. Avoidance of such responsibility is the best reason in the world to stop therapy and stay with a way of life that is most secure.

The second, and more important impact of this family transition, is that the therapist will be out of a job, and will discard thousands of dollars of income that could be had for the asking by simply listening to Bill three times a week until either the trust or the therapist expires.

The proof is in the pudding. In the vernacular, "What you see is what you get." Seeking to establish a healthy balance will require the cooperation of all key players — and the therapists, above all, must be willing to risk loving confrontation. For that to happen, therapists must be ready to exchange killing themselves slowly — whatever the motive is — for having fun!

2

THERAPY VS. THERAPEUTIC: THE MAGIC OF CHANGE REDEFINED

Therapy < ———————————————— > **Therapeutic**

intense	playful
parent	child
role	real
one up — one down	lateral
fixed bounds	negotiable bounds
protected	vulnerable
passive dependent	active dependent
unilateral	shared
authority	responsibility
assigned power	utilized power
trust in	trust with
to talk about change	to risk change
normal	natural

An old farmer told me as a young boy, "Life is simple. You are either living or you're talking." For the purpose of this discussion, therapeutic is to risk change as discovered in "living." Therapy is the "talking" about change — past, present, and future.

There is *no* middle ground. Living is risking the new moment which is always therapeutic, regardless of outcome. Talking may be educational, at best, but still does not produce change.

For eleven years, Seth had pursued personal analysis — three times each week. During his first encounter on the phone with this therapist, Seth was brilliant in the description of his compost pile. He had labeled, dissected, and cross-sectioned — from the leaves atop the pile through the underlying organic mass.

After ten minutes of boredom, the question was posed, "Seth, what is it that you want to risk changing in your life?"

(Long pause.) "I don't know . . . my analyst never asked me that in eleven years."

Magic

In an oversimplified statement, the magic provided by the therapist is much like the black feather that helped Dumbo, the elephant, to fly. It was not until he lost the feather in midair that he believed the words of his mascot mouse: "There was no magic in the feather . . . you were flying by yourself all of the time!"

Magic is the illusion that an energy field outside of Self is in control.

Many believe that energy is dispersed or withheld from a "bank" based upon deeds, works, or just plain goodness. In any case, the center of energy is without and must be sought or earned to be used.

"Why did God take him at such a young age?"

"I'll use the lottery to pay off my debts."

"If the surgery is successful, I'll live!"

Risk is the doing of the energy field within Self.

From this point of view, the gifts within us have already been given. Our energy field may be a product of biological and social genes, learned behaviors, or trial and error. The argument is academic. If the onus of responsibility is upon us to look within for the meaning of change, the result is sought by taking risk.

"To be or not to be; that is the question."

"Love another person as you would want to be loved . . . as you love yourself."

"I AM THAT I AM." (God's retort to a skeptical Moses who asked, "What shall I tell the people when they ask me for your name?" Exodus 3:13.)

The fear of losing the feather is the fear of having to face the responsibility of using our own power — to fly by our Self with only the support of our mascot's encouragement.

Change

Sheldon Kopp's (1) delightful book, *If You See the Buddha on the Road, Kill Him!,* gave us a refreshing new look at the role of the therapist. The typical therapy contract under scrutiny by Kopp is a simple one: one person looking for someone with answers, and another who takes a fee for service without stopping to understand the implicit message of the contract. The resulting "pilgrimage" of psychotherapy must involve debunking this myth if a person's change is to be authentic as well as to last.

An American Indian proverb put the message more bluntly:

Give them fish,
and they will have fish for today.
Teach them how to fish,
and they will have fish for a lifetime.

For therapy (and the therapist) to move in a direction of giving up the magic, and allowing for the fact that persons (not patients) have had the power within all along, is to refocus responsibility for power in therapy from the therapist to the person. How persons have abdicated that power in their own family systems is replayed constantly in their present lives as well as in their therapy sessions. When family members are not invited to understand these competitive power plays, the role of the therapist often becomes that of playing out the roles of missing family members.

Gus came home from Viet Nam angry, isolated, and disconnected. His best friend, Vern, came home in a casket.

It's now 1989, and Gus has still not been able to rise above the tiger cages. The same government that said he should be proud to serve his country keeps him codependent with meager handouts that further minimize his self-worth.

Gus has been through three V.A. Hospitals and corresponding medications. He has been couched by an analyst and irregularly attended a "support" group of other angry vets. Meanwhile, he has lost what little support he had from his family when he came home.

Shattered, not trusting anyone, Gus had returned from the war to discover that his wife, Ruth, could not wait. She had met him at the airport with his close friend, Tubbs, who was excused from Nam with a weeping pilonidal cyst.

As a last measured blow, Gus' children, Meg, 12, and Sandy, 10, had been warned by their maternal grandparents that Daddy was "greatly disturbed," and they were never allowed beyond that barrier. During his five-year absence and hospitalization abroad, he had stopped writing, never guessing that most of his letters had been intercepted rather than not answered.

The several therapists that had moved briefly in and out of Gus' life had all noted, in elaborate detail, the extent of Gus' severed ties from his family. Yet none, over the course of twenty years, had once thought to recommend that his estranged family join him in therapy.

With well-meaning intentions on the therapists' part Gus had recoiled in fear from any of their attempts to reach him. Each attempt to tamponade the hemorrhaging internal wound only resulted in covering up the infected area and leaving each therapist personally full of remorse.

A suicide would have brought the family together for a brief moment in time, and it wasn't as if that were not a possibility for Gus. More hidden from view, however, is the therapists' suicide. When attempting to be a rescuer, unable to play the many roles missing in Gus' family, the well-meaning therapists became engulfed in the same pit of quicksand.

The saddest epitaph of all, perhaps, is that most therapists cannot conceive of calling a meeting of their own family to discuss feelings. With this unconscious block firmly in place for the therapists, the family reunion for Gus never was a possibility — except in death.

Redefinition

My dream is that the therapists' role, in the timeworn psychoanalytic sense, can be changed dramatically. That instead of the pseudo-parent role which allows the "child" to be one-down (vulnerable), therapists will become consultants to persons — working within the family systems.

Proposed, an oversimplified redefinition: a *therapist* is any person willing to meet with only fragments of the family. In so doing, the therapist, regardless of how skilled, is unconsciously drafted into playing out roles of the important persons who are missing. The more closely these "roles" parallel unfinished business in the therapist's life, the more handicapped the therapist becomes in working with the fragments of the family. A *consultant* is any person committed to working with the team as a whole and who has more regard for life than to waste it while pinch-hitting with a losing team. Because consultants bring ego deficits of their own, like holes in a slice of swiss cheese, a team of *co-consultants*, balanced for gender as in Noah's Ark, can better insure covering each other's "holes" when working with a family.

Consultants, while acting as catalysts, will assist family members in the nurturing and support of each other. They will help family systems begin to share and learn with each other. With the family itself acting as its own therapist, movement of feelings becomes lateral instead of one-up or one-down. As the families begin interacting with each other, the co-consulting team is freed from "goal-tending" responsibilities and are better able to attend to their consulting.

Specifically, most parents have modeled well the act of being responsible for their children, allowing the children freedom to explore their own being within a protective environment. What children have typically not experienced, as they mature and become ready to leave home, is how to be a parent to their parents; that is, that parents can cross over, however temporarily, and receive nurturing and support in place of their usual role of giving. This sense of cross over, being a learned event, is one that is rarely experienced. Children move on to become parents without having ever learned.

Is it any wonder then that we have been confined to exactly the same model in therapy?

Therapy, as past evidence supports, provides the same necessary mythical parameters that the therapist will "be responsible and one-up" in order to perform the necessary "surgery." What is uncertain is the amount of spurious placebo effect contributed by the therapist/parent myth which is used for anesthesia.

Certainly one possibility is that the definition, over the years, of what is therapeutic vs. therapy, has evolved as the therapists' own comfort level has allowed. As mentioned earlier, a comparable definition of "alcoholic" is that the diagnosis becomes appropriate at such time as individuals begin to drink more than their doctors do. It may be that we have defined "therapy" as a place where therapists are comfortable enough to seduce the "other" into an intensive sharing of "secrets," be paid for being the interested voyeurs, and do so under the flag of "professionalism."

The story is told of a psychologist administering the Rorschach ink blot test to a "disturbed" individual. Every ink blot that the individual described was an unusual sexual aberration. When he finished, the astute psychologist reported, "It appears that you have some deep seated sexual disturbances in your life."

"How can you say that?" came the reply. "They're *your* ink blots!"

If the consumer were to ever discover that his neighbors have lived with the same fears, have not shared those fears because of pressure by the same social mores, and furthermore, could derive a lasting positive change by "unloading" those fears to each other, helping professions will face a major overhaul.

A similar parallel may be found with oncologists — our friends in the medical profession whose specialty is cancer. Every oncologist who has been in practice longer than a year knows and has heard of a dozen or more "miracle" cures in which the person became so enraged upon being pronounced terminal, that they immediately commence a crusade to make any changes necessary to live — AND DO! Yet for unexplained reasons, or perhaps even unconscious motives, the oncologist will not use these persons as a referral support group for other persons wanting to attempt such radical changes. Why?

One local oncology center said that the whole idea was frivolous and not sound treatment planning, that it only gave persons false hope and helped to foster denial about the *fact* that they were dying. So who is dying? And who really knows that they are dying? Sometimes it's hard to tell where denial begins and leaves off.

Therapeutic

For the moment, consider the definition of therapeutic to mean any process from which lasting growth and positive change occur. That, furthermore, the intensity of an experience in any setting will be the synergistic sum of the persons' energies involved, and the collective responsibility directing those energies.

Collective responsibility of all persons will include:

1) having, for the moment, selected designated therapists who are more, rather than less, aware of their own resistance;

2) having selected at least two designated therapists at any given moment as a safety measure to keep each therapist from becoming hooked into taking responsibility;

3) providing a safety net of trust that conveys a sense that no one will be allowed to disrupt the positive energy flow;

4) concentrating on the "here and now" as a thinly clad metaphor of past, present, and future transactions; and

5) not attempting, as a therapist, to contain the interactive energies of persons within the group, but to yield control of that responsibility to group participants, as that most closely replicates reality; a group is only a temporary surrogate family that helps build a bridge back to reality.

Consider, finally, that any group has an interpenetrating psychic energy field within which a trust element is sensed. Since participants will usually, at the onset, "assign" that trust to designated therapists, much of the sense of trust that a group has in any setting is conveyed by the unconscious aura permeating from those designated therapists. The group begins at that level and then builds its own aura which will, in turn, control both the intensity and the level of self-disclosure.

Bruce Taub-Bynum (2) has dared to describe this phenomenon in print. The family energy field is ". . . a matrix of implicit energy vortexes" through which members signal other members without conscious filtering. Much like the bumper cars at the county fair, our embodied vehicle stays connected above with an extension rising from our vehicle to an electrical net above the arena. When jarred off the net, our vehicle becomes inert until reconnected.

In the Polynesian religions, the Kahuna exists in Spirit form about 18" above our physical being. These Kahunas carry on the real essence of communication while our conscious minds create diversions away from these Truths. Therapists are tangential consultants to this family process, but not active participants.

The Moment of Risk

A family system typically enters therapy with a low trust level often related to the distribution of power (the responsibility for decision making) that has caused its collapse. The process of therapy is commenced with the hope that the therapists will assume that power and reorganize the family system so that it works. When therapists themselves are duped into believing this myth, they unconsciously impede the very process which they had hoped to enhance.

The bottom line is that change does not happen as a result of education. Change happens only in the moment of taking responsible risk. When families experiencing that risk are willing to discuss their experiences with other families who have already lived through changes of their own, the courage and support needed to dare the moment of risk are available for the taking.

By combining family systems, when therapists are trusting enough to yield their implied power, a multiple families group becomes a set of mirrors that will reflect more honestly than therapist or therapy team. From this ever changing vantage point, family systems evolve, as they choose, to restore their own sense of power, which brings with it the inherent trust to leave therapy and fly with their own magic.

REFERENCES

(1) Sheldon Kopp. *If You See the Buddha on the Road, Kill Him!* New York: Dell Books, 1969.
(2) E. Bruce Taub-Bynum. *The Family Unconscious.* Wheaton, Illinois: Theosophical Press, 1984.

3

KEEPING THE FAMILY IN BALANCE: WHY FAMILY DYSFUNCTION WORKS

"What in the world happened to you? How did you manage to get two black eyes?" exclaimed one friend to another.

"You're never going to believe this. We were standing up to sing in church when I noticed this rather fat woman in front of me with her dress caught in her rear. She looked so uncomfortable that I reached over and pulled the dress out for her."

"That certainly explains one black eye," replied the friend, ". . . and how did you manage to get the second?"

"Well, we stood up to sing another hymn, and I noticed the dress was stuck again. But this time, my friend standing beside me reached over and pulled it out. Acting quickly, I said, 'No, no . . . she wants it that way!' and tucked the dress back in for her."

What a perfect metaphor for the so-called "dysfunctional" family. From all of the benefits of training and experience, professionals have developed the skill to pronounce families in need of change — in spite of themselves.

An inverse proposition is that there are no dysfunctional families — only dysfunctional therapists who try to intervene when *they* believe a situation is not healthy. In whatever crazy manner a family has learned to function —

to stay in balance — the family has found a way to survive.
Like all adaptive mechanisms, the balance is life sustaining.

Balanced Imbalance

In Chapter I, this state of impaired homeostatic balance
in a family system was described as *functional dysfunction.* One of the identifying characteristics is that the system becomes tenaciously more rigid when faced with confrontation or intervention by well-meaning therapists.

Therapy purports to remedy all dysfunction. Yet, often in
the process, families leave dedicated to maintaining status
quo, and therapists become dysfunctional ("burned out"
in the pop art sense of the word) in trying their best to
fix them.

A story is told of two dolts, posing as hunters, who came
upon a wily nude woman in the underbrush of the forest.

" . . . and what are you two boys doing here?" she
inquired, leaning back seductively.

"We're hunting . . ." said one.

" . . . wild game," replied the other, finishing his
sentence.

"Well, I'm wild, and I'm game," sighed the nude — at
which point they shot her.

Taking a family at face value and making a "therapeutic
diagnostic evaluation" is often no more than a projective
impression that does more to block channels of communication than to open them. A close friend and colleague said
that he had quit making diagnostic evaluations when, in
reviewing his records over a period of time, he seemed to be
evaluating only himself and his dysfunction of the day.

Consider several alternative assumptions about families for whom the label dysfunctional is used:

Diagnostic Projection

1) No matter how well supported by both theory

and experience, a diagnosis is a subjective and immediate judgment call coming from our own present gestalt.

Alexander Pope, an English author, was once quoted as saying, "'Tis with our judgments as our watches; none go just alike, yet each believes his own." The Germans say all of that in a word: **gestalt**.

While the powers that be (American Psychiatric Association, in this case) have tried to delineate objective criteria (the DSM III, etc.) for consistent diagnoses, therapists are still limited to their own gestalt. That ever present "filter" only allows access to data that is already on board in the mind's computer. Where there are no reference points stored, there is no acknowledgment of data being received. In an alarming way, one's ability to diagnose is constantly hampered by this Catch 22 continuous loop of "What you see is what you see is what you see . . . "

For example, dentists have typically responded to the TMJ (temporal mandibular joint) syndrome as a physical issue that could be addressed and corrected with some degree of success as an engineering problem. With a correctly fitted bite plate, proper orthodontics, supportive attention, and possibly surgery, the problem and accompanying pain could be lessened over a period of time. For those dentists willing to explore new horizons, learning about stress as both a primary and secondary contributor has accelerated treatment and prognosis.

Now comes research (1) from the homeopathic school of medicine that with all instances of TMJ, buried deep within the person's physiology, is the herpes zoster virus that contributes directly to the condition. By diagnosing and treating the virus, pain and other symptoms are alleviated within a few weeks, still leaving the physical and emotional issues to be addressed, but making the task more manageable.

Functional/Dysfunctional

> 2) Functional and dysfunctional are only com-
> plements of each other just as one person's
> ceiling may be another person's floor.

Dysfunction, while there is some common ground for agreement, is basically no more than a best guess made by a therapist or treatment team so that a baseline may be established from which to commence "treatment."

As a rule, in most therapeutic modalities, this judgment call is made in private, without the benefit of including the "patient" — much like pork barrel politicians who cut their best deals in the back room. About the only saving grace of this model is that it saves embarrassment for the treatment team as they argue and discuss their way to a conclusion. This also models healthy disagreement for those therapists who were raised with none.

Depression, for example, is often the center of heated debate as to its origin and treatment. Does it stem from chemical imbalance that can be autocorrected with lithium? Is the "innate" tendency for depression part of the inherited family tree? Can depression be caused by stuffing anger? Perhaps as theologians have tried to educate us for years, depression is simply being apart from God — "hiding from" in the cold shadows, apart from the warmth of His love? Or is depression always loss related? After years of controversy, the fight still continues — each of the disciplines ignorantly promoting their own piece of the truth.

Seventeen-year-old Denny has been in a private psychiatric facility for nearly a year. His mother has serious concerns that Denny will " . . . do himself in . . . " if proper care is not given. During the eighteen months prior to his hospitalization, Denny had encountered three major losses in his immediate family.

When his oldest brother enlisted in the Marines, the family gave lip service approval. However, his father left shortly thereafter, to be with another woman, leaving Denny's mother as a helpless victim. Within the same month, Denny's paternal grandfather (who was the primary source of nurturing in Denny's life) died. To make matters even more difficult, Denny's best friend, Tony, had overdosed on drugs just a year before Denny's brother left.

The diagnosis: chronic depression with thoughts of suicide. Treatment plan: long-term (as defined by the insurance company's ability to pay) hospitalization. Keeping Denny alive has become a total preoccupation with Denny's mom, relieving her from both grief and anger over her divorce. The third sibling in Denny's family, a sister, Denice, who is ten, has been largely ignored through all of the circumstances. She is excluded by the treating psychiatrist because " . . . she might misunderstand his (Denny's) suicidal ideation." Meanwhile, she is an accident looking for a place to happen.

An old rabbinical tale is told of an angel assigned to carry Truth in a basket to Earth. On the way, the angel stumbled and fell. Truth, caught in the wind, was scattered to all corners of Earth. The hungry recipients below each scrambled for their own piece of the Truth, waving frantically and shouting with glee, "I have it . . . I have it . . . I have found the Truth!" Treatment teams, beware!

Indian philosophy tells us that the sum of the parts is always greater than the whole. Not unlike a jigsaw puzzle, one fragment can only lend clues to the surrounding pieces. It is only when those interlocking pieces are connected that the bigger picture begins to appear. To examine each individual piece of Truth under the microscope for its inherent value is to miss the bigger picture.

"Out of chaos comes enlightenment." — Tao

   3) Dysfunctional is often a misnomer for the chaos which accompanies change; yet such chaos is a necessity for the enlightenment which follows.

The American public has been totally duped into believing that anxiety, discomfort, and pain are all negative pieces of chaos. Consequently, the focus has remained upon covering the symptoms rather than inquiring as to their origin. Annual U.S. sales of valium and alcohol, two of America's favorite masking agents for such symptoms, are phenomenal. These symptoms are a natural part of the immune fail-safe system. To mask these symptoms is to eliminate the valuable clues that identify the underlying illnesses. Even the newest of automobile operators would not consider covering one of the distress signals on the instrument dash of their car. Yet, those same individuals would, without thinking twice, cover up a similar distress symptom in their body.

Families, hurting, in a similar manner, are quick to seek help for the distressed member of their family, but would resist with fervor seeking help to determine what the scapegoat member was "acting out" on behalf of other family members. So the chaos becomes the vehicle that eventually brings the family together in spite of themselves.

A Balanced Equation

4) Chaos is always a balanced equation just as enlightenment is: not being able to comprehend the magnitude of either may seem to give cause for the label "dysfunctional" to be applied.

When families focus on one hurting member, and insist that they are invested in change for that individual, there is simultaneous resistance to that change being made for the simple fact that one change evokes another. Any singular member in a family network who changes will cause a necessary shift to happen, in a domino effect, with all other significant members in that system.

Helen's call, as a distressed Mother, was not an unusual one.

"It's my daughter, Lucille. I'm very concerned about her. She has dropped out of graduate school and is unable to find work."

"Where is your daughter living?"

"She has recently come home to live with us, and that is causing a lot of conflict between my husband and me. He wants her out."

"And what keeps you holding on?"

"She has incredible pain with her lower back and cannot afford the recommended surgery. I have already borrowed from *my* savings to help her because my husband won't."

"How is Lucille paying her other living expenses? How does she get around?"

"Lucille is still driving the car that her father bought for her sixteenth birthday, but it's about to fall apart. She can't afford to get it fixed on her Social Security disability income."

(Slow on the uptake:) "How old is your daughter?"

"Thirty-nine."

Unable to focus upon their own demise, Lucille's parents, in their late sixties, trapped in an angry marriage of forty-nine years, have now centered around a "dysfunctional" daughter. Their lives, in fact, have been centered around Lucille since her conception four months prior to their marriage.

Life viewed from Lucille's unconscious, may have a different perspective. If your single source of constant care in your life is approaching death, why not let them know that you can't make it without them?

The family never commenced therapy. Lucille refused to come.

This phenomenon is due in part to the fact that the "hurting" member of the system is acting out feelings for the entire network — a principle similar in nature to the lightning rod. The lightning rod, contrary to what most believe, does not attract lightning, but rather dissipates the electrical charge on the building that would eventually become strong enough to bolt upward to electrically charged clouds. By discharging this electricity evenly from the lightning rod system, the major lightning bolt never occurs. The hurting member of the family has, therefore, come to serve a functional purpose for the entire system, and unconsciously, the entire system comes to have a vested interest in maintaining the person in that role.

Many therapists, who see individual members of the family, have learned this lesson the hard way by finding that the more they attempt to "fix" the hurting member, the more they experience being undermined by a seemingly supportive family member. What has, in fact, happened is that the so-called dysfunctional family has been functioning without the therapists by whatever adaptive means the family has been able to find. When the therapists attempt to intervene, they are met with resistance as the outsider who is going to ruin their "functional" system — even though the family's stated goals are diametrically opposed.

Timing is Everything

5) As believed in Eastern philosophy, when the student is ready, the teacher will appear. As family systems are ready to emerge from their chaos, they will find the needed strength, support, and direction to do so.

Therapists, again as a by-product of their training, have been trained to respond to anyone who asks for help, regardless if the accompanying behaviors are in opposition. The current number of "burnout" workshops attest to the impossibility of this task.

A baseball coach, in his right mind, would never attempt, in his wildest imagination, to offer his services for pay to work with only six members of a team who decided to show for practice, especially if three of those six were not speaking at the time. Yet therapists blindly forge ahead, prostituting themselves to work with any part of the team who shows.

This behavior is most commonly justified by the education theory — that somehow we can teach those members of families who say that they want change in their lives to reach those members who don't. Witness the fact that in this piecework modality, individual members of the same family network are often in therapy, by themselves, for years on end talking about family members who are not present at the time. *Education does not cause change. Change occurs only when an individual risks doing something different, and the family system can adapt in such a way as to tolerate that new behavior.*

While this process provides a livable income for therapists who are primarily acting as expensive friends until the family decides to talk with each other, the changes are slow to come and cost-ineffective. However, with years of training and experience invested in this archaic system, to say nothing of personal livelihood, therapists are reluctant to be honest about their motives. When the consumer public and insurance companies become aware, change will occur swiftly.

The Process of Change

6) Therapeutic intervention (more appropriately called therapeutic grandiosity) is a process, which by necessity, includes collusion with the family; without collusion, there is no intervention.

There is an interesting story told about a nonconforming sparrow who decided not to fly South for the winter. However, persuaded by an unusually cold winter, he reluctantly started his journey. In a short time, ice began to form on his wings, and he fell to earth in a barnyard, almost frozen. A cow passed by and crapped on the little sparrow. By now, the sparrow thought that it was the end.

But the manure warmed him and defrosted his wings. Warm and happy, able to breathe again, he started to chirp loudly. Just then, a large cat came by, and hearing the chirping, investigated the sounds. The cat cleared away the manure, found the chirping sparrow, and promptly ate him.

The story is said to have at least three moral lessons:
1) Everyone who shits on you is not necessarily
your enemy.
2) Everyone who gets you out of the shit is not
necessarily your friend.
3) If you're warm and happy in a pile of shit, keep
your mouth shut.

Therapists are a part of a time-honored profession
which consistently tries and retries to extricate people from
their shitpiles under the pretentious flag of insisting that
these people are unhappy — often another personal projection of the therapists. It's as if there is an unwritten code
that families should not live in shitpiles, much less appear
to be warm and happy there.

The lesson is often learned only when countless hours of
energy have been expended to save another's life, who then
disappears without warning, leaving the therapists with
less of their own lives to live.

Summary

Perhaps if there is an accurate use for the term dysfunctional, it should be applied to therapists who continue their
exploitive practices in the face of evidence that the therapeutic process is greatly accelerated when the entire team
shows to play, and that winning seasons become a predictable event.

Most likely, the law of supply and demand will force the
needed change. When the consumer public becomes enraged enough, the power and responsibility for change will
have returned to its rightful place in society: the family
system.

REFERENCES

(1)   David Baker, Th.B., D.O. From a lecture about the
nature of herpes viruses. Philadelphia, Pennsylvania.
December 13, 1987.

4

WHAT IS A HEALTHY FAMILY?

In a culture that prizes competition over creativity, normative definitions are a necessity. For most, comparison to a norm begins even before birth, and early childhood is thoroughly saturated. Who walks first, talks first, and speaks in whole sentences first is greatly emphasized. By these standards, Beethoven would probably have been considered retarded.

Starting school only further hypes the myth with the added burden of "grades" awarded for how well one matches the teacher's own abilities. Early readers in my first grade experience were designated as bluebirds. Slow to rise to the occasion were cardinals while those who could not comprehend at that time were the crows. Assuming that unconscious implication is a much stronger teacher, I was probably directed toward the color blue as my favorite and initiated with my first indoctrination of color discrimination for the color black at the same time. True to form for such ignorance being promoted, several of the crows have moved on to brilliant and creative careers, not withstanding a few years of stigma.

Education is moving slowly toward *non*-games, beginning to reward right brain activities, and slowly understanding that non-whites don't perform well on white I.Q.

tests. But change is painfully slow and will require a major overhaul in cultural thinking about education, religion, psychology, government, and medicine.

Illness vs. Wellness

The illness model, which emphasizes disease and treatment rather than health and maintenance, further underscores the elusive mythical norm. For becoming ill, a person is rewarded immediately with additional love and concern, time out, drugs, and sympathy. For demonstrating emotional stress in a manner not acceptable to the family norm, the reward is time out in a resort which may range anywhere from an economy community crisis center to an exclusive club, often in excess of $1000 per day.

The major absurdity is that Americans actually congratulate themselves because they only succumb to two colds and one flu per year. The "norm" is an immune system that operates 80% of the time. Again, would anyone be pleased with such performance from their mode of transportation?

So, now that everyone has the message, "wellness" is available on every street corner. Never having admitted to a longstanding focus on illness, the helping community now reacts with renewed vigor toward "making people well" without ever asking whether or not they have chosen a lifestyle that supports living rather than dying.

The pertinent question here is the one raised by Bernie Siegel, M.D. (1) that few have acknowledged yet as important.

"Do you want to live?"

"If you want to live, what are your short-term and long-term goals?"

Ironically, whether the focus is centered around wellness or illness, the immune system is still often ignored. Living and dying are not addressed by professions who have yet to confront their own issues about how they spend the precious moments of their *own* lives. The bigger picture of achieving balance, health, and wholeness is a natural event, not a normative one, and must be addressed in that manner.

In the early 1970's, I was hired as staff at a facility specializing in the treatment of adolescent schizophrenics. My most important lessons learned were under the guidance of a "cracker" character who resembled a jovial, used Santa Claus. Armed only with an eighth grade education and unable to even spell schizophrenia, much less understand it, Al was brilliant with the kids. Leaving the explanation and treatment to "the degreed folk," Al treated the kids with loving firmness as if they could accomplish anything asked of them.

Charley was a case in point. Removed from a posh ($10,000 per month plus in 1972) treatment center on the Eastern seaboard, and placed in this low-budget facility to work with Al, Charley rebelled immediately. Frightened and disgusted by Al's request to help cook breakfast, Charley did his best catatonic routine in the common room while the other adolescents watched in wonder, and ate.

When that ploy didn't work, Charley went out to lay down in the busy intersection of traffic in front of the facility. When the others had finished breakfast, they all went to the curb's edge to applaud and cheer Charley. Having failed at that, Charley returned to the common room to do an even more impressive rendition of a catatonic freeze.

The punch line was saved for last. About an hour into the catatonic stupor, Al brought a friend over to meet Charley.

"Charley, this is my friend, Diane. She wasn't here when you did your thing in the street this morning. Would you mind terribly going back out there to show her?"

Charley responded by picking up a nearby Coke bottle, hurling it through the plate glass window, almost hitting his parents' new, beige Cadillac. They had just arrived for their first visit. With Al clearly in charge, and the first sign of healthy anger emerging, change was already underway.

One would think that such innovations in treatment would draw immediate attention to a "natural" instead of a normative approach; yet, nearly twenty years later, this treatment facility still exists as a unique rarity.

The Norm and The Misfits

The normative model also brings with it the approach/ avoidance fear of being found out, causing most to play their cards close to their chest. A friend of mine once worked in a setting where comparing compensation was grounds for being fired. This religious institution, touting itself as an Equal Opportunity Employer," paid on two scales — one for members, and one for non-members.

The fear of being a "non-member" in any group re- presses sharing and the consequent discovery of common denominators, so the system becomes a self-perpetuating one. On the eve of the first astronauts' flight over the "dark side of the moon," Erik Sevareid made an astute observation in his evening commentary (paraphrased from memory):

> Today we discovered, to the chagrin of many, that there are no humanoids living on the dark side of the moon. Instead, we photographed just so much more dust and craters. That no man's land, so richly fantasied throughout history, is now commonplace. Perhaps the day will soon come when mankind can share their own dark sides to make the same discovery.

To understand the "healthy family" is to risk making this same discovery. If, for only a brief moment, disrobing were allowed, an instant awareness would be experienced: all humans are quite the same and uniquely different. Both the sameness and the difference must be prized.

Natural Balance, Not Normative

There is a natural balance in every family system that

may be as well defined as the balance in any other observed system in nature. Any force, either from within or without the system, acts as a catalyst for change.

The child must die for the adolescent to be born and a similar death again occurs as adults individuate into their own person. Because there are few exact pronouncements of such events in our culture, or rituals to define their beginnings and endings, the impact of such changes is even more critical. From a simple Golden Rule perspective, such change is addressed by the healthy family to determine what will best keep the system intact during such evolution.

Health, according to the Navajos, is "Walking in balance." In a simplistic manner, this Indian belief emphasizes the interactive relationship of all of the pieces to the whole. No Indian would have ever been found urinating upstream in a river from which they were going to drink downstream later that day. Their teachings of "Never take more than you need," and "Leave it the way you found it," could still be deemed as an important discovery for family systems — to say nothing of ecology.

Some natural, everyday courteous extensions of those "laws" are:

1) If you borrowed it, return it in the same condition or better;
2) If you turn it on, turn it off;
3) If you broke it, fix or replace it;
4) If it isn't broken, don't fix it;
5) If you enjoy receiving gifts, give them;
6) If you enjoy freedom, be responsible.

and so on.

Basically, these laws are no more than a reduction of Christianity's Great Commandment, or the central truth of any major religion that has survived the test of time.

Healthy natural balance in a family system must include awareness and interaction of all internal systems including physical, spiritual, sexual, social, mental, and emotional.

In turn, such awareness forces a constant defining and
re-defining of boundaries — both individually and as a
system.

Boundaries

When any member of a family system defines the
boundaries of their freedom and accompanying responsibility, the space of important others is immediately affected.

Sylvia is a typical fourteen year old. She has begun the
painful task of individuation within her family by defiance.
When Lenin declared that " . . . rules are like pie crusts;
they are made to be broken . . .", he must have been raising
his own adolescents.

Sylvia's mother believes that her daughter should have
the freedom of expression to establish her own rules.
Sylvia's father believes that Sylvia should exhibit being
responsible first. Trapped between two dissenting parents,
Sylvia has quickly learned the meaning of leverage.

By playing Mother and Father against each other, Sylvia
can guarantee a base of operation against which to formu-
late her own laws and opinions. Following much the same
ploy of the cartoon character who throws a rock in between
two friends to watch them fight over who threw it, the
distraction of battle can be a helpful way to minimize the
chaos of puberty. Anything less would mean that the entire
family might have to confront the passage of a child leaving
home, to say nothing of the rites of sexuality that precede.

Robert Frost (2) could have easily been writing about
family systems in "Mending Wall." Two New England
neighbors have a seasonal discussion over restacking the
flat rock wall that marks the boundary with the pine cones
and the apple orchard on either side. One insists that the
boundary is necessary; the other constantly wonders aloud
why a wall is necessary when the apples and pine cones will
not bother each other.

Freedom and responsibility are necessary complements
of each other. These negotiated boundaries form a tempo-

rary structure that gives everyone a sense of individuality as well as a reminder of participation in the system. Whether America's offshore coastal boundary is twelve miles or twenty is irrelevant. That other countries agree to mutual respect over an agreed upon boundary is an absolute necessity. How families observe these boundaries, and survive changes, has much to do with their ability to be flexible. This elasticity is an absolute necessity for any family who is going through change without disintegrating in the process.

Elasticity

A family's ability to stretch and grow, to give and take, throughout periods of change, is one of several healthy vital signs. Much like knee socks beginning to sag, members of a family system who lose their ability to flex and spring back, will falter as well.

A singing group named the Spinners perform a memorable piece during their show called "Rubber Band Man." During the song, the singers are connected by giant rubber bands, all interconnected at the middle. As one person pulls back, a relative tension is placed on each of the others to move with him. As another moves into the circle, the reduction of tension causes the others to momentarily lose their balance and fall backwards.

Virginia Satir did a similar exercise in her training workshops using a long continuous piece of rope to wrap around family members showing all of their multiple connections. When finished with wrapping the family, she threw the remaining end of the rope into the audience to demonstrate their connection and dependence upon the community at large.

Whether a family remains connected or becomes isolated has much to do, as well, with how they laugh and play together. I have yet to see a family system whose presenting problem was that they laughed too much or were playaholics.

Laughter

Humor is more than the spice of life; it is the very glue that gently wraps all of the pieces in an intact package. Like rubber cement, humor is resilient and elastic. Humor is the first element of family life that deteriorates, and the first element needed to restore a family system that has become fragile.

"Why, exactly, did you bring your parents for this interview?" I inquired of the resistant seventeen-year-old daughter (who was currently residing in a juvenile detention center).

"Me? I didn't have anything to do with this. I don't even have phone privileges here."

"Well, that's strange," I countered. "I could have sworn that you called this meeting because you were concerned about your parents' marriage not making it."

"How did you know that they are always fighting?" she asked, surprised.

"Oh, just a lucky hunch . . . but then, they have probably gotten on much better with you out of the way now."

"That's not true," she replied quickly. "My brother says that it's living hell there . . . things have actually gotten worse since I left."

"So . . . you were concerned enough to have a meeting, but you just put Mom up to calling."

"I hadn't looked at it that way, but I do worry about them."

"Perhaps they would be better off locked up here until they get their differences settled. I'm sure that your brother and you could take care of things at home until they are better."

She smiled knowingly, then broke into laughter. "You're strange," she said warmly.

In just a few short moments, the tension is out of the air, and the family begins to look and laugh at itself. Healing has just begun.

Those comedians who invoke the most universal response in us are those who poke fun at the same hidden moments of our beings. George Carlin elaborates on " . . . sneaking the groceries that we don't want back onto the shelves — trying not to get caught." Aging, as seen through the eyes of George Burns, all of a sudden becomes joy rather than drudgery. Robin Williams has perfected the art of catching us with our guard down.

The sooner that we return to laughter about these hidden common denominators, the sooner we return to the playfulness and health of youth.

Play

The medical profession has long been aware that play dilates and energizes the human system. Blood flows more freely to feed necessary tissue, body temperature is elevated, and necessary adrenalin released. The immune system, which allows healing to be a constant, is at its operative best when we play.

Yet recess and time-outs are eliminated from our schedules long before high school and the onset of adulthood. Suggesting to the average adult to shut down for five minutes of every hour would seem to imply the need for a national economic recession. The Italians' four-hour lunch break and the Mexicans' siesta have always been misconstrued by Americans as just a bit lazy.

Pillow fights, playful wrestling, and stuffed animals are not often found in most professional therapists' offices, yet they offer families the simple beginnings of a return to natural balance. To paraphrase an old cliche, the family that plays together, stays together. Playing, singing (not necessarily in tune), and dancing have been all but eliminated from our customs; their return is a must.

Dance

The story is told of Jennifer Beals, who when training for her role in *Flashdance*, asked the dance instructor if she would ever be able to dance like the dancing legend, Isadora Duncan.

"I cannot teach you to dance like her," the instructor replied, " . . . but if you place your hand over your heart, you may learn to dance to the rhythm of your own soul."

Humor, play, dance, and creativity are all initiated from the same source; primarily, the spiritual side of the human being. These resources are either promoted or stifled by the family system who lives or dies together, respectively.

Historically, dance has been an important part of ritual for healing, saying hello and goodbye, and sending the spirit, at time of death, on its return voyage. While it's difficult to pinpoint exactly where this special pheno-menon became lost in the shuffle, a revisit to its importance is timely.

Creativity

"All systems are go," a phrase coined by the space age, could even better describe the foundations of creativity. When any part of our system, individual or family, has deteriorated, creative energy is affected.

Rollo May (3), in *The Courage To Create*, has posed an interesting complementary position to Tillich's (4) *The Courage To Be*. Creating extends far beyond the reaches of Being, according to May. To be in touch with our creative forces is to be in touch with our potential craziness. The cutting edge is always at the boundary of what is and what might be. The inherent risk is all that separates the two.

Bill, a friend from California, has entertained my family with laughter, sharing stories of his youth — myths about what he thought made him so different. Bill had attained his current height of 6' 5" at an early age, and also, had the unusual distinction of growing up as an only child on a sailboat which his father had built. Attributing his lack of acceptance by his friends to these characteristics, ex-plained for much of his life, why others shunned him.

For me, the myth of being a skinny 97-pound weakling

with Coke bottle glasses explained the same differences. The fact of the matter was that Bill and I, as children, and needless to say, as adults, are different! Having nothing to do with his height and bulk, or my frail frame, the differences were what Thoreau described as " . . . marching to the beat of a different drummer."

In more recent years, both Bill and I have come to terms with those differences and have managed to surround ourselves with loving companions who are also different. The risk is still the same — that in taking a risk to be, to feel, and to create differently, we will be isolated and estranged — but then, that is the abyss of the creative unknown.

Touching

Until a few years ago, I was also concerned about being too needy — craving more touching than most seem to desire. Then I happened upon a research article discussing this same phenomenon in children who are born Caesarean.

It seems that those infants, who do not experience the last squeeze of the vaginal canal during birth, continue to be needy the rest of their lives, and continuously search for more hugging and holding. I was so relieved. I remembered immediately the scar on my Mother's abdomen, and finally had proof positive that my need was legitimate.

My position was further strengthened by a subsequent article indicating a similar kind of need in Caesarean mothers, who, themselves, remain depressed long after delivery because of not experiencing natural childbirth. The article even discussed the availability of support groups for such mothers; my heart leapt with joy. My mind sped ahead and began fantasizing about commencing support groups for Adult Children of Caesarean Women — a new cult for needy people who, as I, need to explain their irrational acts of needing to be touched constantly.

The myth was wonderful while it lasted. Then came the

day when my Mother was visiting in Florida, and accompanied me to a multiple families group. The occasion presented itself, and I boldly expounded on my findings concerning the need for touch.

My Mother, more than bewildered, broke into a puzzled laugh. "You weren't Caesarean . . . that's an appendicitis scar!"

Ashley Montague (5) in his compelling book, *Touching*, documents thoroughly the need to be touched. Starting with early arrivals in the animal kingdom, Montague discusses the fact that baby rats, when not thoroughly licked after birth, will die. While human observers had for years thought this behavior to be a "cleansing" act, they discovered later that the licking was a stimulation to the digestive tract lest the babies die of bowel impaction. Apes, who are observed combing each others' hair to discover and eat the "nit" parasites growing there, were thought to be just loving each other. However, when the parasites were removed, and the skin of the apes consequently not groomed, the apes developed skin disease.

The skin, as both Montague and Virginia Satir point out, is the largest organ of the human body. While touching serves many functions for humans, one of the most basic is that circulation in both the toucher and the touchee is increased upon contact. As a general rule, increased circulation means all related parts of the human system are better fed.

Where families are observed who touch on a minimal level, or have stopped touching, a parallel breakdown in the communication of feelings has already occurred. Families who touch less communicate much more on a cognitive level, and touch is usually associated with goodbye, good night, or leaving in general. No wonder that touching and the fear of loss often go hand in hand?

The healthy family is one whose touch is allowed on all channels including spiritual — the willingness and ability to "sense" each other and respond without words. If circulation is indeed affected, then a family with greater circulation (pun intended) is a healthier family.

Being Responsible

The inherent willingness to own responsibility for one's behavior is the keystone to any system functioning at its best, be it corporate, psychosocial, or genetic family.

"The dog ate my homework . . . " has always been one of my favorites even though I have not owned a dog for more than half of my life. Flip Wilson's " . . . the devil made me do it" also comes in handy as does substituting "parents" in place of Satan. This works especially well with mothers, who have always been held to be more responsible.

Organized religion, in general, has been helpful with the Pope, being the Father of Fathers, used many times as the fall guy. This is an appropriate extension of the Judaic-Christian patriarchal model. Even in the face of the last decade's movement toward equal rights for women, God is still generally acknowledged to be male.

Educational institutions do not take the blame as well except for poor sex education and hyperactive kids — but then the school board has not yet offered to provide condoms for kids or ritalin for teachers.

Perhaps the best mirror offered by the projective blame of irresponsibility is that we come face to face with our most intimate friend and most passionate enemy simultaneously. That is, the person that we are most likely to blame or embrace is the one to whom we are most closely bonded.

Children provide just such a mirror. These narcissistic depositories of our dreams, faults, joys, and irritations are a constant source of adoration and revolution. It is as if, in a moment of insanity, we have elected to reveal to the world our most sacred vulnerabilities — an irreversible decision, at that.

Striving toward a healthy family system is to risk open confrontation with our children, and to closely examine the introspective look which they offer. "Children should be seen and not heard" rhymes with "divine right of kings." Repression can only lead to delayed explosion. When such confrontation happens in the extended family system with grandparents and children in the same open forum, we, like

Scrooge, have a prophetic opportunity to look into Self Past and Self Future. Most of all, this awareness gives us the opportunity not to repeat history, but to be creatively responsible for doing something new — and healthy.

Summary

The healthy individual and the healthy family system is one which prizes all of the elements discussed above — first in themselves, and finally, in those whom they love. The first sign of imbalance is the critical condemnation of elements in those around us which we are afraid to experience in ourselves. To risk experiencing together is to enjoy healthy relationships — both within our personal system of balance and that of our family.

REFERENCES

(1)   Bernie Siegel, M.D. *Love, Medicine, and Miracles.* New York: Harper and Row, 1986.

(2)   Robert Frost. "Mending Wall" *in Modern Verse in English: 1900-1950,* ed. by David Cecil and Allen Tate. New York: Macmillan, 1958.

(3)   Rollo May. *The Courage To Create.* New York: W.W. Norton, 1975.

(4)   Paul Tillich. *The Courage To Be.* New Haven, Connecticut: Yale University Press, 1959.

(5)   Ashley Montague, *Touching: The Human Significance of Skin.* New York: Columbia University Press, 1971.

5

THE FAMILY AS THERAPIST TO OTHER FAMILIES: FAMILY TO FAMILY

When Gerald Ford lived in the White House, Johnny Carson was heard to quip one evening, "Perhaps Jerry's greatest accomplishment in the White House will be to rise above Grand Rapids."

The same observation could easily be made about therapists. Perhaps the best that could be accomplished in their lifetimes would be to rise above their beginnings, both personally and professionally.

Sid had wrestled with his fear of the opposite sex since age ten. Male relationships always seemed safe.

Forced into an early marriage at seventeen by an "accidental" pregnancy, matrimony was followed by a quick succession of two additional children.

When Sid found the fourth pregnancy terrifying, he retreated to the safety of same sex. Urged to seek therapy by his wife, who only knew him to be in trouble, Sid was assigned the psychiatrist in charge at the local Crisis Center. Hesitantly, he began to describe the saga of his fears.

The psychiatrist listened as best he could for ten minutes, then interrupted with, " . . . let me just stop you there for a moment, and tell you something. If my own son were to come to me today and tell me that *he* were a fag, I would kill him with my bare hands." Needless to say, Sid left therapy even more terror stricken, now more firmly entrenched in the belief that the problem was all his.

Contrary to early family training, responsibility for the *risk* of change belongs solely to the individual. The immediate family and surrounding community provide support and nurturing during transitions, but *risk* is the moment of truth where change occurs.

This idea is by no means new, but rather quite old. In earlier times, such healthy codependency was the sole means of survival. Staying alive meant depending on individual skills as well as supplemental support from the community at large.

Transfer of Basic Family Values

The family was, and needs to be, the primary therapist to its individual members. Families of the community, in the same sense, are the best therapists to other families. As the family is the vessel which carries the basic values from one generation to the next, the transmission of those values depends upon the vessel staying intact.

Head football Coach Lou Holtz of Notre Dame University wrote in his "Letter to the Next Generation," published in *Time* (1):

> Generally, when we are little, it is unnatural for us to like and respect other people; these qualities have to be taught and developed. An infant is basically selfish, undisciplined, and unmotivated. Give him a toy and he'll cláim it as his own immediately; he won't want to share it with anyone. The qualities that we admire in people — honesty, cheerfulness, thoughtfulness, cooperation — must be learned in the home and developed by society. Our future, in my humble opinion, is contingent upon parents successfully developing these qualities so we can evolve into responsible intelligent, compassionate adults.

An individual cannot stay in therapy long enough to absorb these basic values if they are not already familiar with them. Codependency upon the paid therapeutic community (buying expensive friendships, as it were) is symptomatic, in fact, of the breakdown within the suprastructure of the overall family and community system.

Historically Speaking

In the beginning . . .

For a quick glimpse at our early beginnings, one only need scrutinize the characteristics of the founding pioneers of this country. While bold determination was a common denominator of the settlers, their underlying motives were, at best, a mixed bag. Religious radicals, political misfits, sexually repressed, and prisoners, constituted the majority.

Upon establishing a foothold, the newcomers quickly began to replicate the social and political system which they had despised and fled. The new microcosms began to flourish in a narcissistic reproductive act that closely resembled begetting the next generation without ever stopping to inquire as to the shortcomings of the last. That which the colonists were *afraid of* and *running from* was what they inadvertently were *creating* and *running to*.

Captain John Smith, among the early colonists, took a step in the right direction with his adage, "Those who don't work will not eat." However, the lessons which teach the valuable correlation between freedom and responsibility would continue for many generations to come. Many of our modern systems, such as welfare, still operate in ignorance of this truth.

Freedom and Responsibility

Viktor Frankl (2) once commented, during a visit to the United States, that what America needed most was a Statute of Responsibility on the West Coast. Nowhere is the struggle for a balance between freedom and responsibility more evident than in the Western world. Lip service is constant for a Bill of Rights that espouses personal freedom; at the same time, personal responsibility is completely abdicated to a system reeking with authority. Trusting the European model of an honor system would almost be unheard of in this country. Driving without speed limits, riding the rails and buses without ticket checks, and queuing without crowding, are thought to be impossible.

Instead of providing a viable social model, organized religion has continued the battle for authority commenced on the Continental side. Church and State continue to vie for the superior position — a struggle which settlers were certain that they had left behind. Killing each other in the name of self-righteousness started long before Constantinople killed in the name of Christianity.

Personal vindication in the name of "something" has continued on through our own Civil War and has culminated in the ludicrous with the stockpiling of nuclear "deterrent" weapons. In a panel discussion shortly after the first run of *The Day After*, a gripping movie about the first nuclear holocaust, Carl Sagan remarked, "If you are sitting in a room awash with gasoline, it really doesn't matter whether you have seven thousand matches or one."

One of James Thurber's (3) favorite fables recounts a tale of fun-loving bears who played happily in the forest until one day, two monkeys, named Monkey See and Monkey Do, came to liberate them. The monkeys chained the bears' feet together and told them that from that day forth, they would be truly free — free to do what the monkeys told them to do, and free to say what the monkeys told them to say. After a period of time, they broke from their chains and returned to the forest to play. Thurber's moral conclusion: "It is better to have the ring of freedom in your ears than in your nose."

A constant struggle for balance within the family system revolves constantly about this very issue. Having freedom, either before or without responsibility, is a specialty of adolescents.

Robbie said that he wanted nothing more than to be free. By the time Robbie had made his third appearance in juvenile court, he was sophisticated enough in his description of his oppressive parents to let the judge know that they were "fascist pigs" who wanted only to destroy his youth.

Robbie was in court on two felony charges filed by his family, and was returned to court for a violation of probation.

When confronted by the judge as to why he had broken probation, the response was a familiar one to the judge. Robbie had run away from home and responsibility to "be free!"

When Robbie first met Samantha in a multiple families group, he was immediately aware that he might have met his match. By nine years of age, Sam had already been hospitalized twice for "psychotic breaks" and placed in a special school for the emotionally disturbed. Had Sam and Robbie ever decided to become a team, even Batwoman and Robin would have met their match.

Interestingly enough, as is always the case when one family meets another who has been down the road ahead of them, the change is dramatic. On a first meeting, Sam, with a tone in her voice of " . . . well, when I was your age," instantly made Robbie furious.

How dare she? he thought. She doesn't even measure up to my armpit.

But within minutes, Sam began to coach Robbie on some of the finer points about the family living together as a team, and positive change was already underway. What had been a "psychotic illness," untreatable in the best of hospitals, had already begun to dissipate with the tender loving care of the seventeen-year-old "physician" who had already earned her degree the hard way.

And Then — The Illness Model

As if there were not enough constraints, the evolution of modern medicine has added further limitations with labels of "disease" and "illness." While consensus among professionals seems to indicate that labeling a person's behavior really has nothing to do with change, and that quite possibly, the label has an adverse effect, the need to have a "common professional language" still seems to exist.

With the locus of power in the Doctor instead of the High Priest in the Temple, an entirely new frame of reference has been added for the power to excommunicate. Behaviors diagnosed as chemically imbalanced, biologically mutated, and genetically prone establish a baseline paradigm for treatment and collection of fees which Szasz (4) believes is a continuous loop of self-perpetuation.

The myth continues to be fostered that healing happens from without rather than from within. The instant fix of modern medicine is further promoted. When the modern practitioner says, "Call me whenever you're depressed," they mean well. However, the implied message is that a person should remain depressed to have an association with the therapist. Both therapist and person must let go of this territorial rite which they protect tenaciously.

In doing so, the role of parent and child, of give and take, can become interchangeable roles. Who will be the Parent and the Child at any given moment becomes an issue of shared responsibility rather than assuming postures of adequate and inadequate.

In the multiple families group model, parts of families and their roles, become interchangeable pieces. Just as with Ford's Model T, the cost efficiency becomes quite apparent, and there is no therapy mold to break out of in order to return to the real world.

Parent/Child/Parent/Child/Parent

On a more local level, the parenting model that seceded

to this country was a close kin to the divine right of kings fostered in Europe. Parents, as absolute monarchs, were not to be questioned; children were not to be heard. Those children who were compliant learned little about parenting and a lot about enslavement. Those who rebelled in anger and left home early learned much about forging their own way but with the price of isolation from their families.

Satir (5) described the process beautifully. "We spend the first years of our life being 'too young to'; then, almost overnight, we become full-fledged adults without any experience. We proceed to practice being an adult with our children until they leave home frustrated, and by that time, find that we are 'too old to.'"

Sandy began playing Russian roulette with drugs at age thirteen. She often traded her body to the highest bidder, and the dialogue with her parents was a familiar one.

"You've broken curfew again! That makes twice this week. And your eyes (checking with flashlight) are all red again."

"Mom, you're really making too big a thing of this. I'm not doing drugs, and if you would quit putting me on restriction, I wouldn't have to crawl out of my window to see Tim."

Somehow parents and child both survived Sandy's adolescence. Then, the day came when favorite son, Doug, who had always managed to do as much right as Sandy had wrong, left for college. Sandy, now nineteen and an unemployed high school dropout, enrolled in an art class which interested her at the community college.

A year later found Sandy with her GED completed, sharing an apartment with a friend whom she had come to know through the art class, and working full time in an art supplies store. Her fascination with art had developed well beyond hobby, and her work had already shown well in several exhibits.

It was Sandy who brought her parents into therapy. While spending an overnight at her parents, she was awakened by their loud noises when they returned from a party at three in the morning — stoned!

Through another families' eyes in group, Sandy's parents began to grapple with the number of major changes and losses which had occurred in their family, including the loss of the "bad child," Sandy. The second family had been close to divorce following the "loss" of their two children: one to college and the second in a one-vehicle/motorcycle accident. Family to family, person to person, both families began the long journey back to equilibrium — together!

The therapists did little more than watch, through tearful eyes, as these experiences were shared.

Beginning to Reverse the Mythology: Powerless Therapist — Powerful Family

For those who abdicate their power easily, the therapeutic process is a welcome one. Therapists are trained to be objective, removed, and value-guarded; persons come to therapy needy, dependent, and ready to give the responsibility for their lives away to anyone who appears to be the least bit willing to give them direction. The match is perfect.

Families seek therapy because they appear to be powerless. The members of the family have unconsciously colluded to assign their power to an acting-out adolescent, a temper-explosive child, a workaholic husband, or a depressed housewife. Fearing harbored feelings, they feign helplessness, and are willing to pay anyone who appears to be a knowing Buddha (6). The contract that is struck serves a purpose for both parties until the family members become aware that they had the power all along to control their own destiny — that the exploitation which they sought from the therapist only served to underscore their helplessness.

On a simplistic level, therapists choose to continue reworking their own family issues in front of others who are willing to pay to watch. They are powerless to affect change in any family other than their own.

By contrast, family members who appear to be powerless are duping the therapists. In their contrived confusion, they have become without direction. Yet just as the passive person orchestrates far more power than the active one, passive family members are a powerhouse stuck on dead center, waiting for a crisis to enable their finding a new direction.

Eloise, by her mother's report, had been anorectic since age fifteen. Now, forty-one years old, Eloise is in the sixth month of her eighth treatment program. She is surrounded by a staff of fourteen, including twenty-four-hour surveillance by nannies, to be certain that she stays alive.

Eloise's eighty-two-year-old mother says that she will do anything to keep Eloise alive. A boyfriend hovers at her side who has waited seven years to consummate their relationship because he is afraid that sex would be too painful for Eloise.

Whatever the world record is for the number of years that a human body can survive anorexia, Eloise is out to challenge it. Therapists should regard her as cannibalistic. Eloise smiles knowingly throughout the interview. Only she, and possibly her hairdresser, know for sure.

To interrupt this system without regard for where all of the players fit after the change is to become the next sacrifice for Eloise. For her to change her eating habits alone will more than likely mean that her mother will die; it is Eloise who is doing everything possible to keep her mother alive. To make matters worse, the boyfriend's impotence will be identified, and she will more than likely lose him as well.

Worse than any of those losses, Eloise will have to face the pain of her father's suicide when she was fourteen and the fact that he possibly *did* know what he was doing to her sexually when he came home drunk.

The risk of change and the loss of passive power always go hand in hand. To risk change within a system that wants to maintain status quo is to become powerful in a completely different sense.

Change — To Be Responsible To Risk

Change, in the life of any human, or group of humans, happens for only one reason; that is, the responsibility to risk has been exercised. Risk is always relative to present position. One person's ceiling is another person's floor.

When a family becomes stagnant or static, change is always imminent. To address that change, and the inherent risk involved, is the primary issue. Often, families will unconsciously create diversions with an unexpected pregnancy, a new mortgage, or a geographical move. Only an illusion of "time out" is created; the responsibility to risk must still be exercised. A classic example of taking time out for every human is the act of becoming ill.

Health: Walking in Balance

For the Navajos, illness was simply being out of balance — out of center. Illness, in early American Indian medicine, was always related to change: immediate past, present, or immediate future. According to the Cherokee Medicine Man (Eastern Band), illness brings three important gifts:

1) The need to slow down, to take a time out from the present activities that could not possibly operate without us, and to rest;
2) the need to reach out, and to seek love and support from those around us; and
3) the need to reaffirm belief in a suprasystem, a higher power outside of self.

Having taken those steps, a person becomes ready to risk change.

As the family is the most natural of all support groups, illness is often a signal to return to the family for strength. Where individuals in a family do not have the needed strength or skills to regain their own strengths, and rekindle their own courage, another family is the most natural resource available.

The Family As Therapist To Other
Families Before Therapy

Before therapy provided missing familial support, there was the community — a group of families, without training or professional skills, who knew through their natural sixth sense how and when to provide nurturing. Families lived off the land, and emotionally supported each other.

For many apparent reasons, that nurturing has ceased. Families do not share within their own systems, to say nothing of not even speaking to neighbors on the same block. A deep sense of distrust has developed toward anyone who would touch without being invited, and paranoia, not trust, has become the common denominator.

A Return To What Worked

Peer to peer, family to family, and neighbor to neighbor — pulling together as a team for a common cause — that's what worked. If therapists can begin to support rather than impede this natural phenomenon, the needed nurturing from the community can once again be an established force.

The simplest approach: introduce families to each other and step aside. Ask families if they would like to help another family in need. Don't ever assume that they are resistant to the idea, or that ethics and confidentiality are in the way.

Resistance is always a projection of the therapist. Confidentiality is a way of maintaining trade secrets, both in families and in therapy. To let go of this awesome therapeutic responsibility is to live longer — and to model health for those whom we love.

REFERENCES

(1) Lou Holtz. *"A Letter to the Next Generation." Time*, April 10, 1989.

(2) Mary Harrington-Hall. "A Conversation with Viktor Frankl" in *Psychology Today*, Vol. 1, #9, February, 1968, pp. 56-63.

(3) James Thurber. *Further Fables for Our Time*. New York: Simon and Schuster, 1956.

(4) Thomas S. Szasz. "Justifying Coercion through Theology and Therapy." The Evolution of Psychotherapy Conference, Phoenix, Arizona, on December 13, 1986.

(5) Virginia Satir. "Therapeutic Use of the Self in Relation to Family Healing." A conference held in Maitland, Florida, on November 14, 1987.

(6) Sheldon Kopp. *If You See the Buddha on the Road, Kill Him!* New York: Dell Books, 1969.

6

THE FAMILY RE-UNION: A RISK OF THE *IS*

For Richard Bach, the *Is* is — the sum of all past and future seen in the here and now (1). Einstein's theory of relativity made a feeble attempt to give credence to the same idea posed by a writer in Ecclesiastes 1:9: "The thing that has been, it is that which shall be; and that which is done is that which shall be done; and there is no new thing under the sun."

In the simplest sense, a family re-union is the *Is* — much like the work which Kempler (2) described — the moment of the now (3), there is not necessarily an active precipitating event; i.e., suicide attempt, psychotic episode, etc. The only basic requirement is that all members of the extended family must be willing to risk examining the mythology of the past which will otherwise continue to distance in the future. It is the moment of risk in the *Is* that produces change and growth. As always, the change and growth must start from the inside and work to the outside.

What then are the assumptions made about working with a family, and what is the process that moves a family system toward the *Is* of a family re-union?

ASSUMPTIONS

1) A family has the inherent power for change, direction, and growth within its own system;

2) Family members, when encountering change, temporarily commence adaptive behaviors which provide an interim balance system;

3) When issues of change are not resolved or integrated within the family system, the temporary adaptive behaviors may become permanent;

4) A family member, hurting or scapegoated, will generally seek help individually (inadvertently for the family as a whole) when the temporary adaptive behaviors no longer work;

5) Members of a family system will constantly seek their own level of risk taking — will start, proceed, and finish only what they are ready and willing to do;

6) Co-consultants are the catalysts whose presence accelerates or decelerates rate of change, but does not affect change;

7) Transference and countertransference only exist as a blurred continuous loop;

8) Resistance begins and ends with the co-consultants;

9) Content is for education and understanding; process is for change and growth; taking the responsible risk is the primary issue always being negotiated when choosing on which to focus;

10) Past, present, and future are one; the moment is of the past, and is the future; past and future are illusions of distance to avoid the consequence of risk in the present;

11) The Tao expression "Out of chaos comes enlightenment," could not be more true than in a family reunion; it is in confusion that family members are forced to the inside for their own solutions;

12) There are no individual persons, only fragments of a family (4); to view a fragment apart from the whole is to have, at best, a distortion of both;

13) A spiritual sixth sense field is the cumulative energy

mass of the family system (5); described by Jung (6) as the collective unconscious, this electrical field is the basis of the most profound and most ignored form of communication.

14) Touch is a secondary replacement for sixth sense;
15) As the Chinese already knew, "You can't push the river; it flows by itself."
16) " . . . and in the end, the love you take is equal to the love you make." (7)

RESISTANCE

Who calls the meeting?

Still constrained by an inherited "medical model," therapy most often has begun with one person in the family system becoming dysfunctional, maladaptive, neurotic, psychotic, or scapegoated. As Szasz (8) warns, the diagnosis = treatment = payment for therapy = diagnosis often poses a Catch 22 question that is self-perpetuating. This illness model has also prevented many from close examination of life changes because of the fear of being pronounced mentally ill.

By contrast, the family re-union model encourages families to recognize life changes of all kinds and to confront rather than to internalize the impact. Although an acting out teenager, a depressed housewife, or an executive with a coronary are easier to identify, the symptom usually is the tip of the iceberg with nine-tenths of the mass still below the surface.

Any action (passive or active) within a family system will cause a reaction of equal force. Just as with the laws of physical science, homeostatic balance is the key issue. Any major life change in a family member will cause the entire family system to regroup.

A couple, married forty-two years, moves to the sunny South to retire. In the process, they sell their family home, retire, downgrade to a simpler, less expensive life-style, leave all of their friends and relatives, and move to a retirement community for "fun in the sun." Within the first year, the husband has a stroke and finds himself receiving all of the emotional nurturing that he has complained about "missing" for years. The wife becomes enraged that she has become a trapped victim and must now spend the rest of her days with an invalid. However, she tries to cover her rage with a smile under the guise of being a "good wife." The children, with spouses and children of their own, still live in the North and cannot help with the rehabilitation because of time and money constraints.

In trying to understand the power of such an unconscious, passive event, one must acknowledge that there are some "bottom line" issues that will call a family meeting in all of our families. Death, suicide, and terminal illness are among the most important reasons. Issues that are loss related will even draw larger family meetings than such joyous occasions as birth, college graduation, and moving into a new home. Most often, the identified change which calls for a re-union is the identified change that is the last in a series of other major changes.

The Life Changes Scale (Appendix A) has been constructed to not only help identify those significant changes, but also to visualize the cluster effect of how change begets more change. For most individuals who complete the scale, groups of changes have clustered within certain periods of years with wide spaces of years in between the clusters. Even more fascinating is the "coincidental" clustering found when comparing the charts of individual family members. Even when family members have been separated by hundreds of miles and communication has been minimal, the clusters of changes have appeared to group during the *same* period of years raising many interesting questions for further investigation.

Who calls the family meeting then becomes a matter of how quickly the impact of change is recognized, and how resistant the family is to addressing those changes. Said in an over-simplified manner, of all changes ranging from the celebration of death through the celebration of life, those changes having the most unconscious impact will be met with the most conscious resistance.

Who attends?

The best index of resistance for a family re-union is the rank ordering (usually unconscious) of the significant family members " . . . who will never come no matter what . . .," " . . . who would die first . . .," or " . . . and you would never want those people in the same room together." The descriptors used are the best tip-off to the power, real or imagined, that is assigned to these family members. Said another way, the more unavailable an individual is, the more power, either passive or active, they have been assigned. For a therapist not to acknowledge this premise from the start places the therapist in jeopardy, by implication, of assuming those unresolved roles in the family structure.

The third and fourth generations, if available, are a must — no matter how infirm. Some of the best re-unions have been held in nursing homes and hospitals where family members are finally able to address feelings as a part of saying goodbye. Where the diagnosis of senility or Alzheimer's is present, the sessions become even richer as the non-sequitur metaphors are shared. Where senior citizens appear to be key figures, the re-union will not be held without them, which often translates into holding the meeting where they live.

By the same token, small children are equally important to include. Although they are always seen as disturbing and being in the way, they are spiritual barometers of the sixth sense communication in the meeting just as the elders are. Their "disruption" is an important part of everyday living. How the children engage and disengage is a most important index of family life. In recently reviewing the video tapes of a re-union in which a six-month-old daughter was the youngest member, the baby had an uncanny knack of announcing the mood of the moment and would sleep, coo, or scream at appropriate moments that were much more than coincidental punctuations.

The "hold-outs" — those family members who black-mail by threatening to leave or not show when they know that the meeting will not be held without them, usually are the first to become the focal point of anger. However, it is in this moment of anger that the family often becomes empowered to risk — that which they had been unable to do.

Who pays?

Attendance is only the first barrier. The family must now assign a "quarterback" to help reach consensus about how the re-union will be financed. Age fourteen and over pay. The cost for each eight-hour session does not change with the number of people attending. The amount paid by each family member should be relative to the sacrifice and discomfort that is caused. Those designated as "hold-outs" should bear a greater part of the expense as the fee is paid at least two weeks in advance and is non-refundable after that point. (As of this writing, a re-union paid for in advance has never been canceled.) With an average extended family size of twenty-five paying persons, the net cost per person has been reduced to less than $20 per hour for one of the most intensive, accelerated modalities of therapy available.

Adolescents and spouses not working outside the home must obtain their funds somewhere other than from family — and the funds must be legal. That rule was added after it was learned that one adolescent had raised funds by selling baggies of pot.

Who works?

What must be obvious by now is that more than half the work has already been accomplished before a family ever walks through the door. The core issue of power/control distribution in every family has already been addressed as a function of preparing for the re-union. Now the family members have all assembled bringing with them the roles which they are accustomed to playing. A passive person will usually commence by watching the process and complain later that their needs were not met. The defensive will quickly paint themselves into a corner and the scapegoats assume a contrite position. But the individual family members have taken charge of their power, and their roles will be examined under careful scrutiny during the hours that follow.

RESPONSIBILITY

The best definition of what happens during the reunion is within the concept of responsibility itself: response ability. An assumption discussed earlier places the response ability, the risk taking, upon the family itself. The co-consulting team is a catalyst, but the work agenda belongs to only the family itself. Where families begin and where they end is a product of their own energy and willingness to initiate. Any therapists who ever dreamed of having power to move a family toward goals which they have not chosen should try their skills with the three-generation family. Much like the hypnotic trance, a family "in process" will not move in an undesired direction.

PLAYBACK

All re-unions are video taped (9) and consent is a part of the contract made before meeting. The family members agree to schedule time to view these tapes, in silence, either in their own home or in the co-consultants' office. By reports from families, these hours are some of the most important time spent. Through objectively watching a family on television, the wall of denial is most easily penetrated. As with a movie whose complicated pieces do not commence to fit until three days after viewing, the confusion experienced in the moment of the re-union often does not begin to integrate until distancing has been allowed to happen.

CHANGE

Unlike most linear models of therapy where positive change, movement in a strategic direction, homework, and treatment plan are seen to move a family in a contracted direction, the family re-union is confusing, disorienting, and geometric in its progression. While the family's well-being is always a central focus, looking at the incongruities within a system will always be experienced as confusion. When family members have the good fortune of examining family mythology from the archives as a group, especially with the benefits of the elders' wisdom, the family cannot continue to organize in the same manner. The inconsistencies of their lives and the excuses thereof become laughable, and the family can no longer take its old ways seriously. Gentle, loving humor, not ridicule, obviously plays an important part.

The best news of all is that in a very brief period of time, family members have learned a dependency upon each other for "catching" themselves in their old ways. Individual family members have not only learned to trust their own power but to use that power in an on-going manner that minimizes support from the co-consultants, and maximizes the strength of the family system.

SUMMARY

The *Is* of the family re-union is a moment in which family members examine myths which have not only ceased to work, but have blocked further communication. Through learning a new dependency upon each other's strengths and skills, the family is able to change and grow in new directions which they choose as a system.

REFERENCES

(1) Richard Bach. *Illusions*. New York: Random House, 1977.

(2) Walter Kempler. *Experimental Psychotherapy within Families*. New York: Brunner/Mazel, 1981.

(3) D.G. Langsley and D.M. Kaplan. *The Treatment of Families in Crisis*. New York: Grune and Stratton, 1968.

(4) Carl Whitaker. A multiple families group experience in St. Maarten, The French Antilles, March, 1986.

(5) E. Bruce Taub-Bynum. *The Family Unconscious*. Wheaton, Illinois: Theosophical Press, 1984.

(6) Carl Jung "The Concept of the Collective Unconscious." R.F. Hull (ed.) *Archetypes and the Collective Unconscious, Collected Works*. Princeton, New Jersey: Princeton University Press, 1928.

(7) John Lennon and Paul McCartney. "The End" *Abbey Road*. Hollywood, California: Capitol Records, Inc., 1969.

(8) Thomas S. Szasz. "Justifying Coercion through Theology and Therapy." An address delivered at The Evolution of Psychotherapy, December 13, 1986.

(9) Ian Alger. "Audio-visual Techniques in Family Therapy." In Donald Bloch (ed.) *Techniques of Family Therapy: A Primer*. New York: Grune and Stratton, 1973.

7

SNATCHING DEFEAT FROM THE JAWS OF VICTORY: THE PARADOX OF SELF-DESTRUCTION

From Mel Brooks' memorable classic, *Blazing Saddles* (1), comes this unforgettable scene. Two politicians have conspired to fraudulently acquire vast tracts of valuable real estate in a small Southern town. As a last resort to drive the locals away from their homesteads, they appoint a black sheriff to keep law and order.

As the poor peasant rides proudly into town, he is still somewhat amazed to be so lucky. However, as the time nears for him to be sworn in as sheriff, a lynching begins to stir. The minister begins speaking to calm the nervous crowd.

"As your spiritual leader, I implore you to take heed to what this Good Book has to say . . ." (Interrupted by a burst of gunshot.) " . . . Son . . . " turning with a grim look to the new sheriff, " . . . you're on your own!"

The black sheriff, played with wonderful humor by Cleavon Little as Bart, assesses the danger quickly. In one swift move, he draws his long six gun, places the barrel against his own throat, and in a deep villainous voice says, "Hold it . . . the next man makes a move, the nigger gets it."

Town leaders interrupt. "Hold it, men . . . he's not bluffing."

"Listen to him men. He's just crazy enough to do it."

Little continues. "Drop it, or I swear I'll blow this nigger's head all over this town."

Quickly shifting his voice to upper-range scared, Little continues the dialogue with himself.

"Oh, Lawdy-Lawd . . . he's desperate . . . do what he say . . . do what he say . . ."

Feigning being dragged at gunpoint, Little forces himself down off the platform, the gun still being held in his own hand, pointed at his own throat. Moving quickly through the crowd, continuing his fast paced dialogue with himself, Little disappears behind a closed door.

Smiling broadly with a grin of satisfaction, Little bathes in his victory. "Oh, baby . . . you are so talented . . . and they are so dumb!"

Dumb Like A Fox: The Art of Manipulation

The scene is a familiar on to most families. Adolescents, trying desperately to force their parents into providing structure, often point the gun at their own throats with the same quiet desperation. And parents, who mean well, often appear dumb to the con that is going down.

"You can't stop me from dating him. He is the only one who loves me, and you can't take that away from me, too . . . no matter how strict you are!"

"Just for that last smart remark, you will be on restriction another week!"

"Well, isn't that just great! My total restrictions now add up to more than three months."

"Does that include the weeks' restriction from last week when you left the house in the middle of the night through your bedroom window to see Billy Bob?"

"No, but it doesn't matter . . . I would have left again last night if you hadn't nailed the wire over the opening."

And so it goes — child claiming to want adulthood, but throwing it away at every chance. Parents swearing that they can hardly wait for their children to leave home, yet quickly relieving them of any responsibility by trying to impose impossible rules.

So what exactly does this paradox mean that often results in self-destruction?

Codependency

In the whole of the animal kingdom, codependency is fostered among human offspring for the longest period of years. Now ranging somewhere between sixteen and thirty years, (depending whether or not you are supporting your child through medical school with a specialty) is this unprecedented community attachment that has altered the history of generations to come.

A very distant second is the chimpanzee family. According to Jane Lawick-Goodall's (2) studies, with only two years of close dependency, the chimp never leaves his community except through severe injury or death. They mate with only one mate per lifetime. The chimps hunt, travel, and nurture as a tightly clad group. What chance, then, do humans have after twenty plus years?

"I would like to set an appointment for my son," requested a concerned mother. "He's not eating right, won't get up in the morning, and has dropped out of school. Some mornings, I have to cook his breakfast three times and throw out the first two, just so he will have a warm meal."

"How old is your son?"

"Twenty-seven," came the reply.

Before trying to determine what chance humans may have, codependency, as a measure of health, must be defined. The simple laws of physics apply — as in teeter-totter.

A teeter-totter, one of the simplest mechanical devices, only works when weight and weight distribution on either end of the board are balanced. For a smaller individual to be in balance with a larger person, the smallest weight must be furthermost from the center, and the largest weight, nearest to the center.

If either individual moves in any direction, ever so

slightly, the other must immediately move to compensate. This delicate balance is the key to why the contraption works.

Likewise, should one person decide unilaterally to climb off the board, the ride is over with a jolt for the other. Certainly any person with elementary experience with a teeter-totter chooses the ride knowing that these simple laws are in effect. Yet, the teeter-totter has never been billed as codependency nor advertised as anything but fun.

Did someone explain the disclaimers to you, prior to your first ride? Were you told that if you enjoyed the ride too much, that you would be seen as unhealthy? Have you ever been approached to enter a support group for people who have *too much fun* really enjoying teeter-tottering? Is there a treatment center covered by insurance in your neighborhood for those who have ridden too long?

The clamor to be the first on the block (pun intended) to receive treatment for codependency has only been exceeded by the media blitz of advertising which sends you scouring the family to find the addict and the enabler. It's as if each family must have a closet person addicted to something, and a complementary person who tracks on that addiction.

A telephone request for a referral came, asking, "In your opinion, which is the best local treatment center for codependency? However, before you answer, I must tell you that I will only go to the one which is covered 100% by my husband's insurance. He has already refused to pay for any more treatment programs."

The question, as usual, is the answer. Codependency, by definition, involves at least two persons. When that second person is a therapist, the unhealthy imbalance simply traps the therapist into playing out the worst fears of the person paying the therapist's bill. Or worse yet, the anonymous third-party insurance company pays — as if we had nothing to do with paying them, or our premium rates being increased simultaneously.

Even with the addict and the enabler present together, the odds are not good that they will stop the continuous loop which makes their two partial egos, one whole ego.

Members of their family system, who have in parts, either watched out of fascination, or looked away with fear or boredom, must find a new way to be with this favorite couple, or else be doomed to unconsciously perpetuate the same dance.

"My son is twenty-seven, and I'm terrified that he is back to using drugs," a frightened mother reported by phone.

"Why do you think he's back on drugs?"

"He's been hallucinating for the past three days. I was so afraid, that I moved out of my apartment. The rent is paid for the next sixty days, and if something hasn't changed by then, he's going to need professional help."

Enslavement or Isolation?

Taken at its worst, the two most feared extremes of the codependency spectrum are enslavement or isolation. In the most healthy moment of codependency, the individual is always moving between these two extremes.

If one identifies too strongly with the original family system, that person will never become an individual and separate out from the system. The advantage is the extraordinary care and attention which that person learns to receive/extort from the system — usually more from one individual than from the rest of the system.

The disadvantage is the sameness with other family members that will never allow the individual to become uniquely distinct within that system.

Isolation, the other boundary fear, comes when an individual family member sets out to reinvent the wheel without any help from those generations which have preceded. Rather than take the chance of being seen as " . . . one of the . . .," the individual will go to any extreme to look or sound different.

Paul Punker, with his red rooster-tail hair style, has no trouble being seen as "different" from his Madison Avenue-styled dad. Both feign utter contempt for the other's dress code, yet they are as connected as two cats who have had their tails tied together and are hanging over a clothesline.

Carol Compliant suffers from the same difficulties, as the community will applaud conformity long before dissent.

Oddly enough, most dissenters immediately find a group of "like kind" with whom to comply, and thereby, help to ease the isolation from the family of origin. The young rebellious character who has found acceptance only by straight-arming his family and the community, invites the ultimate disaster. While shaking his fist in contempt at his family and community, telling them that he " . . . wants no one to tell him what to do . . .," proves to them, once and for all, that he is in charge, and joins the Marines or marries a shrew.

Andy was one such character. Andy had been overweight since just prior to the onset of puberty. Had anyone taken the time to explain the natural presence of physical change, at least part of his fear might have been diffused. Worse yet, secretly comparing his penis size with his friends in the cold showers following physical education, Andy's worst nightmares were confirmed.

It had seemed to Andy since age twelve that he could do absolutely nothing right. With Father yelling at him from the time he arrived home from work, Andy would head for his hiding place in the back yard until his father would settle into his daily drunken stupor.

Prior to puberty, Andy had always had wonderful care from his mother. She had tracked religiously on his every whim and had given him everything that was within her reach. But even she was not ready for handing the new bar of soap through the bathroom door, and seeing the new dark hair that adorned his body. She made it a point to never make that mistake again.

Had Andy's mother ever learned to confront his dad, the matter might have been a brief one. But she excused her husband's abuse of alcohol with fainthearted excuses like the stress of his job or that he had never been paid what he was worth — a slight projection, to say the least.

So, Andy joins the Army. Penises, compared in a cold shower, are all still the same, yet all look bigger than his. His mother writes, but he misses her tender looks and words. His new father, the drill sergeant, is even more abusive, and bludgeons him with his worst fears — that maybe he really is a homosexual.

On the evening of his fifth attempt to graduate basic training, he commits suicide by hanging himself with a sheet in the barracks during recreation period. His body is shipped home with full military regalia — and honors.

Ethnic Logic

In deference to my dear friend, Marybeth, I have converted to the term, ethnic.

Actually, there is nothing ethnic about it. Every society has had its token dolt. In Germany, the dolt, in ethnic jokes, is Flemish. The point is still the same. There are times when the human species, regardless of cultural background, uses a backwards kind of logic to justify the absurd.

Nixon, whose ethnic background still escapes me, said that the Watergate coverup was in the " . . . best interest of national security." He, also, as President, justified the bombing of Hanoi " . . . to save the people."

Jane Fonda, playing the same role as the youngster in "The Emperor's New Clothes," who had identified the King as being naked while clothed in his splendid, new expensive suit, was taken to task for her honesty by self-proclaimed Patriots. Nixon, meanwhile, even with all of the acknowledged foul play, will be remembered more dearly by history than Fonda.

In Greek theater, the ethnic dolt was called the "fall guy," a character who could be sacrificed for the integrity of the plot. Regardless of identification, the major purpose in the life of an ethnic character or fall guy, is that he saves the day by forfeiting life itself.

To date, there are no treatment centers for the "victim" enablers — only the addicted who can be identified. And while Joan of Arc has some small place in history, most kids will sooner remember the taste experience of a burnt marshmallow in a bonfire.

Why, then, is self-erasure so prevalent? Adolescents always give the best answer.

"If I kill my dad, I will go to jail. If I tell my mom the truth, she won't believe me. I would rather be dead!"

And dead is in the majority.

Ways to Die

General Douglas MacArthur once said that age has nothing to do with death. You are simply dead when you have no more dreams.

In *The Buzz Aldrin Story,* a movie which barely made it to the box office, the astronaut, who was the second to set foot on the Moon, depicts the horrors of attempted suicide, when at age thirty-seven, he found that he had nothing else for which to live.

Having dreamed of becoming an astronaut since age five and having achieved the pinnacle of his success, this national hero was willing to take his own life rather than dream a new dream.

Rollo May (3) in *The Courage To Create,* said that a person reaches their ultimate craziness in the moment of creativity. In that moment of reaching over the edge of reality, where no person has ever stood before, the human is stretched toward God, in whatever manner that ultimate form of energy may be described.

When Christopher Columbus apparently seduced Queen Isabella into financing his crazy venture, more than dollars changed hands. Can you imagine walking into a map store, and asking to buy a map to the New World? Everyone *knew* that the world was flat and that the abyss below ate ships for lunch.

Where did this crazy Chris get off venturing to dream such a dream? And why did he ever bother to tell anyone else, knowing that he was immediately qualified for the loony bin?

Out of Chaos Comes Enlightenment

The dream, when it happens, occurs first in the moment of madness.

Joseph, an early Jew in exile, would have certainly qualified. Joseph, known for his dreams, began reporting on his new visions during his imprisonment in Egypt. He was going to become the Pharaoh's right-hand man.

Sure, Joseph! Hallucinating again? Probably the prison food. And to whom do you tell that one — and how? Carefully! The bad news was that the dream took several years to be fulfilled. And to whom do you talk in the meantime while you wait? It is not unlike the Atheist who was having difficulty achieving orgasm because there was no one to talk to —.

The old Tao expression, "out of chaos comes enlightenment," certainly could not be more true, but then who would ever take comfort in that belief in the middle of chaos? Enlightenment never meant much in the middle of an anxiety attack.

Killing in the Middle of Chaos

An old fable tells of a scorpion, who is about to drown on his flooded island home. Seeing a frog nearby, he attempts to befriend the frog for a favor.

"Pardon me, Sir," cried the scorpion. "I know that we have not always been the best of friends, but I will surely drown if I am left here. Would you mind if I just climbed up on your back, and rode with you across the water back to the mainland?"

"You must be joking!" replied the frog. "Not only are we natural enemies, but just as certainly as I agree to do you such a favor, you would sting me and I would die."

"Foolish frog! I may be your enemy, but I am not stupid. Why would I kill my only friend . . . I would certainly drown along with you."

"You are absolutely right," said the frog. "Forgive my

distrust of you."

And so the journey to the mainland began. The waves were high and strong. Several times during the journey, both thought that their time had come. But the frog struggled valiantly, and the scorpion managed his best to hold tight.

Finally, the waters began to calm, and the lights of the shoreline became visible. Both the scorpion and the frog began to relax and enjoy their certain victory.

It was at that moment that the scorpion drove his poisonous tail into the head of the frog, and the frog's body began to paralyze.

"Why did you do it, you fool? Why did you kill me, your only hope, and bring about your certain death as well?"

"I don't know," replied the scorpion. "I guess it's just my nature."

One of the few predictable directions of the unconscious mind is its known ability to push away what it is that is most needed. In the moment of craving affection, humans will generally break off their most important friendships.

Elisabeth Kubler-Ross (4), a Swiss psychiatrist who has spent more time than any other professional with families experiencing a death of one of their members, has reported some interesting findings that best define the self-destructive nature of the unconscious. Having been involved with more than ten thousand families with a member who was actively dying, six thousand of whom were children, she stumbled across the following statistic.

Within one year of the loss of a child, more than 70% of the parents divorced. Where the child's death was by suicide, the divorce rate exceeded 90% within the first year.

If this process of selective isolation were to be chosen consciously, one would have to agree that disengaging from one's primary support group, on the heels of such an incredible loss, would be poor timing at best. With the overwhelming personal pain of losing a child, why would any person opt for divorce at that time?

Yet when post interviews with these individuals were conducted, the standard reasons for divorce were given; i.e., she liked to sleep with the window open, and I liked to sleep with it closed. Very few recognized that the loss of a child was in any way related.

With some kind of illogical logic, the unconscious is making its best bid at protecting the frail human from one more unexpected hit. It's as if the unconscious is saying, "I'm going to have to kill you now so that you will never leave me by surprise."

Ways To Live

When Freud estimated that over 90% of our decision making is made at an unconscious level, at first reading, the estimate sounds a bit high. Modern science seems to be pointing to "too low."

Less than twenty-five years ago, before the advent of micro chips and biofeedback equipment, science taught that the autonomic nervous system could *not*, in fact, be overridden. Indian fakirs, whose experience indicated otherwise, were called fakers instead by the Western world.

In the late sixties when Neal Miller demonstrated that a rat could simultaneously raise its pulse and lower its blood pressure, he, also, was placed in the category of faker. Only a few years later, he had trained another rat to raise its pulse rate in one ear, lower its blood pressure in the other ear, and maintain both stable in the body at large.

To drive his point unquestionably home, he then injected the rat with curare which paralyzed its involuntary muscle system, and finally, decorticated the rat, severing the rat's primary link with the brain. The rat could still perform the same functions!

Today, the use of biofeedback, though not fully supported by the medical community, is commonly used to control diabetes, epilepsy, blood pressure, and anxiety.

Choosing to live is to opt for the responsibility of taking charge. The optimum fear addressed in doing so is that such an act of risk sets a new benchmark with such emphasis that the individual can never return to what was.

Whether it be a commitment to relaxation training with biofeedback or calling a family re-union, the yield is always directly related to taking the risk.

The Norstrom family is a case in point. One of the most common themes playing from one generation to the next was that the husband and wife would split with a mass of unresolved anger hanging in the air. The children, trapped in a canyon with a forest fire raging on all sides, would come to believe that the world was really a smoke-filled canyon and that they must have had something to do with having started the fire.

With the same certainty of biological genetics, that child, upon becoming a parent, instructed the offspring, by example, that the world was indeed a smoke-filled canyon. They then continued the myth, in fact, by separating early in their own marriage.

The first break in the chain of events finally came on the eve of leaving home for an adolescent whose family was in the fourth generation of this repeating pattern. Her preparation included flunking her senior year, not receiving a diploma, and attempting suicide in front of a family riddled with fears of previous suicides.

A family re-union was held with more than twenty members, all ex-spouses included, arriving from seven different states. It was the first such family gathering that had occurred without a wedding or death.

The meeting started cautiously with all of the appropriate social graces. Old scabs were left untouched, and possible sore spots ignored. After the first eight hours, the gloves came off and the therapists were asked to leave. For the first time, this family had the courage to confront each other with love, anger, grief, and joy — and best of all, lived through the process.

Anger, when released appropriately and timely, is as healthy as laughter and pain. *Love, without anger, is not trusted. Anger, without love, is separation.* When anger is held inside for more than fifteen seconds, we move toward being ruthless killers. Unable to justify killing with conscious premeditation, the venom retained will become life threatening. Whether the resulting death is recorded on the final certificate as suicide will only be a matter of timing.

Anger, like laughter, develops and needs to be released on a moment-by-moment basis. Most people would not consider consciously withholding a bowel movement. But all would quickly recognize the symptoms of pain that accompany that choice and be "moved" to take action immediately. For those who have held in laughter (usually where laughter is inappropriate), pain is also quickly recognized. Or perhaps more individuals could relate to not farting around others which is even more inappropriate than the times in which we are not allowed to laugh.

Speaking of discomfort and gas, all sewage being processed by anaerobic bacteria gives off gas in the process. This gas is both lethal and explosive. When we come to view our angry sewage with the same kind of respect, we will all live happier and healthier lives.

Summary

Self-destruction is anger turned inward for lack of a more appropriate outlet. Usually masked as depression, both our physiology and chemistry have been temporarily, and sometimes permanently damaged prior to the final destruction. Simply put, suicide is killing the wrong person.

To become aware of this lethal enemy who lurks within, and to learn to channel the enormous reservoir of energy being constrained, is to free an equal amount of loving energy for use in healthy relationships.

REFERENCES

(1)   Mel Brooks, Norman Steinberg, Andrew Bergmen, Richard Pryor, and Alan Uger. *Blazing Saddles*. A motion picture written and directed for Warner Brothers by Mel Brooks, 1974.

(2) Jane Lawick-Goodall. *My Friends, The Wild Chimpanzees*. Washington, D.C.: National Geographic Society, 1967.

(3) Rollo May *The Courage To Create*. New York: W. W. Norton, 1975.

(4) Elisabeth Kubler-Ross. Presentation during five-day seminar in Oviedo, Florida, on death and dying, 1983.

8

LIKE A MOTH TO THE FLAME

The moth is a quick study as the original "fatal attraction." While the flame is beautiful and soft, this flickering beacon means certain death to the soft, winged creature who seems to almost be aware of impending doom as it circles just one more time before sizzling to a crisp.

No one is quite certain yet what kind of biological clockwork triggers the self-destruct mechanism, but the attraction toward what we inherently know to be lethal to our system is not just limited to moths.

Lemmings seem to live a rather content life for relatively long periods of time when they suddenly become overwhelmed with an urge to go for a swim, i.e., drown! With the same determination as the moth, like cattle stampeding without any sense of direction, the lemmings rush into the sea in droves and take their own lives.

In a world becoming inundated with "addictions," there seems to be one simple definition that is a constant. An addiction is the repetition of a behavior which has detrimental effects, *knowing* that the consequences are not only

*This chapter is dedicated to all of the wonderful alums at Janet Greeson's "A Place For Us" who have had the courage to conquer their depression through finding the necessary love and support with a network of nurturing others who *are* there when needed.

harmful, but in the end, possibly life threatening!

The story is told of a man meeting a friend and noticing that he had acquired a severe burn on both sides of his face.

"What in the world happened to you?" he asked immediately. "Oh, I wasn't paying attention when the phone rang, and I answered the iron." replied the friend.

"So what happened to the other side?" the man continued.

"They called back!"

_Co_ Dependency

As discussed briefly in earlier chapters, the focus has too long been on the dependency and not on the _Co_. A little discussed fact exists that a person with any serious addiction of any nature _must_, by definition, be involved with a _Co_ who is willing to spend unusual amounts of time just tracking on the behavior of the addicted.

In the more serious stages of addiction, the _Co_ must become responsible at all levels as a price for such fascination — emotionally, financially, physically, sexually, etc. The addicted cannot _choose at some level_ to be responsible for necessary life needs. That such creatures are always paired with the same certainty as the creatures on Noah's Ark is worthy of a study itself.

Schizophrenia

In working with schizophrenic adolescents and their families, a diagnosis usually considered quite distant from addictions, this paired phenomenon becomes quickly obvious. Any human, in such a withdrawn state, would soon die without any of the daily necessities. Much like the helplessness of an infant, this condition will quickly attract the need of a caretaker whose life becomes focused upon rescuing the individual. As the rest of the family watches helplessly, the matched pair become bonded and inseparable.

In a treatment center in central Florida discussed earlier, a young psychiatrist had the courage to pioneer a method of treatment rejected by earlier mentors. He cautiously selected six male and six female adolescents who had been so diagnosed, put them in an old house next door to his office, and hired a couple without prior experience or knowledge of schizophrenia (1).

As an initial agreement prior to commencing treatment, the parents agreed to have no contact for the first thirty days. Only after that period of earlier assessment would a decision be made for family contact. What often seemed to be a miracle occurred during that first thirty days. Surrounded by other adolescents without their Co's present, the youth soon began to turn to each other for support, always within the bigger framework and comfort provided by the "tough love" of the surrogate parents. Yet when they returned home for even a brief period of time, they would often return in a worse condition that when they had entered the program. Soon, the program was modified to begin including parents, grandparents, and other relatives so that all could become involved in the necessary supportive changes.

Strange then that the experts in the academic world still spend precious time fighting over the origin of this condition. Studies have been plentiful since the late 1930's defending biological, chemical, and psychological origins. For the family who spends most of their waking hours tracking on finding a solution, the academic question is a moot point. Here is a model that has worked successfully for twenty years and is still a well-kept professional secret.

I have personally always liked Ben's explanation best. When Ben arrived at the center with his mother, she constantly used the word "carry" to talk about transporting Ben. While it would have been easy to trace the word to a Virginia plantation background, the phrase turned out to be more than descriptive.

Ben's mother, fearful of the "overdose" of ether which he received at birth, literally carried him for the first four years of his life until his weight became prohibitive. She had taken him from one specialist to another looking for a diagnosis that would explain why he had never learned to walk! Each specialist had a distinctly different opinion, but none that were satisfactory to Ben's mother. As the relationship continued to become more enmeshed, Ben's father withdrew more and more from the family as did Ben's overachieving sister. There were further complications in that the father had never wanted to have a second child and urged his Catholic wife to obtain an abortion without the church's permission when he learned that she had "tricked" him into the pregnancy.

By the time Ben was brought for treatment, he had been diagnosed as schizophrenic, catatonic type, and was all but immobilized in his rigid posture. Two and one-half years later, it was a proud staff who interviewed Ben at discharge. The director of the program, after sharing with Ben how proud she was of his progress in school even while holding a twenty-hour-per-week job, said, "Ben, exactly what do *you* think happened? What was the turning point for you?"

With all of the innocent straightness of Peter Sellers playing Chauncey Gardner in his last movie called *Being There*, Ben paused and answered wistfully, "When Winter ended, and Spring came bringing fresh flowers and sunshine, I began to notice a big difference in my mood. Yes, it was Spring!"

How change is described may be quite irrelevant when it's all said and done. The critical test is that change has, in fact, happened. But that also might lead to further confusion as to whether healing is really an art or a science.

Allergies

There is a growing amount of evidence that the human body physically craves what is most destructive. Chocolate, wine, salt, eggs, and dairy products seem to head the list. Many experience difficulties with foods only at certain times in their lives and then are never bothered again, which lends even more intrigue.

Diabetes

Sugar has been a culprit in many diets long before it was identified. Adolf Hitler was said to have sugar hoarded in every residence, office, and vehicle which he used, much like an alcoholic. For many, including Hitler, sugar appears to act almost like a toxic substance. How the body ingests sugar directly affects other areas of metabolism and may result in diabetes or hypoglycemia. The question still left unanswered is about the timing of the onset. What exactly has happened that triggers that onset?

Alcoholism

Perhaps no other field of study has received the necessary attention that alcoholism has. Studies have prevailed since the early 1920's. General consensus is simple. Given *any* type of treatment — inpatient, outpatient, half-way house, residential, *or even no treatment* — the stats are about the same. Approximately 50% of the population will stop drinking to live and the other 50% will die prematurely.

The Co Enabler

What then is the driven motivation of the enabler to "save" the life of another while sacrificing their own?

The story is told of a dedicated codependent who is drowning, going down for the third time, and sees someone else's life flash before his eyes.

Rita, just married for the fifth time about two years ago, says that she is the victim of "bad coincidence."

At seventeen years of age, Rita left home because her father was alcoholic and was given to fits of rage in which he would severely beat her mother and her. Without any modeling from her mother, Rita felt that she was left with no choice except to run away from home.

Rita is now forty-two and married for the fifth time. As all four husbands were alcoholic and given to fits of violent rage, she was at least aware of a pattern before the fifth try. She swears that she lived with her present husband for two years during which time he never drank and never raised a hand in violence. During their first week of marriage, he came home drunk and beat her severely. Should she go for a divorce?

When Rita began to examine her patterns leading up to matrimony, the light bulb finally came on when asked, "Well, where would you go next to meet someone single?"

"The same place that I always go," Rita replied quickly. "The XYZ Lounge."

From vaudeville, the reminder of a depressed woman who told her friend, "Whenever I'm down in the dumps, I get a new hat!"

"Oh," said her friend, "is that where you get them?"

Not unlike the story of the scorpion told earlier, it's just our nature.

The Twelve-Step Solution

Without a doubt, the Alcoholics Anonymous twelve-step program has offered more love, nurturing, and support in the twentieth century than all of the churches and synagogues combined. Not unlike the American Indians who believe that the most important part of healing has to do with a belief in a higher power, the AA model insists on the same.

Regardless of the addiction, there is a twelve-step program available both for the Dependent and the Co. From adolescents to tots, any age, any time, any where.

What needs to happen next is for the homogeneous groups who all meet separately to form one large group in the same room where each can reach out to the other. While family groups are cautiously being tried, the general attitude has been, "Why mess with something that works?"

There is an experimental program presently in the planning stage, for example, to bring rape victims and their families together in the same room with perpetrators and their families. Too much significant data is lost without seeing the systems in their entireties.

For the past five years, The Chrysalis Foundation, Inc. of Winter Park, Florida, has been providing several experimental training groups that are all multiple families —that is, entire extended families meeting together to provide needed support while growing through changes. While many addictive type situations are presented, the groups are by no means limited to that. The point is that the Co and the Dependent as well as their entire families work in the same room together quite well and form a multilevel support group that is incredible.

As most groups accumulate experience with age, a core of wisdom evolves that is a stockpile of everyone's spirit who has left their footprints in the process. It is in the midst of that security that families experiencing changes of their own can grow and be nurtured at their own pace.

Healthy Co Dependency

For some reason, since insurance companies have begun to cover Co Dep treatment (as it has come to be known), the entire concept has skyrocketed out of sight. Groups have sprung up on every corner and Co Dependent has almost become a slur.

While the term "interdependent" has been used to describe the healthier aspects of connectedness, that word somehow misses the importance of the "pair" discussed earlier.

Consider the possibility of *healthy* codependency in the relationship of a pair.

Imagine a coin flipped one hundred times. The statisticians tell us to expect fifty heads and fifty tails. That's balance. While occasionally a fifty-five/forty-five will show, sixty/forty is beginning to be rare, and seventy/thirty almost never. The further that the ratio moves from fifty/fifty, the more off center the balance becomes.

By the same count, imagine a giving/taking relationship

that begins to be off center by the same numbers. The further away from center the relationship moves, the angrier *both* persons become. *Either giving too much or taking too much fosters the same anger and all of the unhealthy expectations that accompany.* To stay healthy is to stay in balance.

The Model Is The Message

Is it any wonder that with therapy still being conducted primarily on an individual basis that changing code-pendency as a way of life takes such a long time? Individual therapy is perhaps one of the best living models of codependency in existence.

Think about the cost efficiency of paying an expensive friend who is willing to listen for a price while you discuss all of the important people in your life who are never there for you. In addition, you have some strong feelings that they may even be the cause of your pain.

Worse yet, what often occurs are several members out of the same immediate family system hiring several coun-selors for individual work to all complain about each other. Now the therapists themselves are in a double bind as their ethical considerations will not allow them to discuss these newly learned secrets with each other.

Is it simply too practical or cost efficient to imagine that these persons could all be in one room together without being designated as "patients" and that if the paid profes-sionals could stay out of the way long enough, that "person to person" might actually work?

Therapists' Resistance — The *Only* Resistance

One possible reason that families do not congregate to help each other as they did prior to therapy being available is that trained professionals are *themselves* afraid of the process. Most professional counselors, when asked, could not conceive of having their own families in a room together.

A typical family model familiar to many of us is one in which family members pair off to talk with each other in private. Mothers and fathers talk about secrets which the children would not understand. Daughters tell mothers what they want their fathers to know and sons tell friends what they want their parents to know.

The doctor/patient model has many of its attributes patterned after this family model. Doctors talk across to other doctors but often down to nurses and other staff. Nurses, often the housewives of the system, talk with each other but are careful what they say to the doctors. Information given directly to the patients is sometimes not the whole truth because the patients " . . . would not understand."

On the bright side, today's helping professionals are learning new ways, and resistance should be substantially lowered, in time. But change takes valuable time and happens slowly.

Pressure for change in the twenty-first century will come from the consumer and from insurance companies. Consumers are already becoming savvy about shopping for therapists and not turning over their power to just anyone. Insurance companies have already taken the lead by putting pressure on the helping community to continuously defend their treatment modalities. When insurance executives begin to take a more serious look at the "repeaters" who continue to milk their benefits for all they are worth, change will happen even sooner.

When the first insurance company offers 20% coverage for individual therapy and 80% coverage for families, therapists' resistance will no longer be an issue. Just as medicine began to discover fifty years ago that the hip bone does connect to the knee bone, so psychology will be forced to address families as systems.

Summary

What was once commonplace — families helping families — will again be the medium of exchange. When a family system functions as a whole, codependency will move to a healthier level of balance as the "pair" will be dependent upon the entire system for existence. At that point in time, responsibility will belong inside the family for its own members instead of waiting for outsiders to take charge.

References

(1) W.J. Muller, III, M.D. *Journal of Hospital and Community Psychiatry*, Vol. 25:9 (1974), pp. 587-590.

9

PLAYING FOR KEEPS: RESPONSIBILITY IS NO ACCIDENT

Rickie had the only steelie shooter in the third grade. Somehow, from game to game, Rickie always ended up with most of our prized glass cat's eyes. I never learned until years later that Rickie was also a kleptomaniac. Come to find out, it was not just the size of his shooter that made all of the pretty marbles disappear. Playing for keeps is a tough lesson for a kid to learn — even tougher for an adult.

Joan Baez made a similar observation years ago when she sung lyrics about the feared Jesse James gang:

> Some rob you with a six gun
> Some with a fountain pen.

Abdication of Power

When we give away our power and the inherent responsibility for that power, we commit a theft. Always easier to see that it's our friend who is the kleptomaniac; but *we* must participate in the scam by bringing our marbles to the game.

In Florida, the law does not distinguish between the gun-toting hold-up artist and the driver of the getaway car. Both are considered felons and are punished equally.

Alcoholics Anonymous teaches, "One day at a time." When the responsibility for one day seems overwhelming, the day is easily broken into hours, moments, and seconds. *The size of the fragment is relevant to the immediate reservoir of power and responsibility available.*

Robin Williams (1) as private academy instructor John Keating, in the movie, *Dead Poets Society,* instructs his students *"Carpe Diem!* (to seize the day!)" "To seize the day," is to empower and embody the idea with acting responsibly in accordance with what we value as important.

I was several years into my private practice when I received my first legal challenge through the Federal Privacy Act. A brash young attorney, subpoena in hand, arrived at my office with the Defendant's attorney and court reporter in tow for the deposition.

As the Plaintiff, with whom I had previously worked, had already given the attorney written release for information, my refusal to turn over my file of personal notes was a direct affront to the system. While I had agreed by phone to supply the needed information in a written report, it became clear in the opening minutes of debate that such a report was not going to be acceptable.

I was told, at that point, to either turn over the file or the sheriff would be by in the morning for it. I countered that I would destroy the file before turning it over to the sheriff and was then threatened with contempt of court as a backup.

The next morning when the sheriff arrived with the contempt notice, my psychiatrist associate said to me on the way out the door, "There are places to draw a line and fight, and places not to . . . you can't feed your family from jail!"

The judge patiently heard us both out, then looked at me over his spectacles and said, "Would you mind if I looked at the file to be certain that there is nothing being withheld?"

The judge scanned the file for a brief moment, then said to the attorney, "He's right . . . there is absolutely nothing in this file that would be of help to you."

What would have been an embarrassment to many professionals was a welcome relief to me. The judge was even more helpful by reviewing the present interpretation of the Privacy Act. He suggested that any future notes should be in the form of a personal diary without names so as to not be sought for such scrutiny.

I breathed a sigh of relief and followed his excellent advice from that day forward. His words have proven true more than once. Needless to say, the attorney left in a huff.

About two years later, having long forgotten the incident, I was surprised to walk into the waiting room to meet a new family and see that it was the same attorney, his wife, and children. We both broke into nervous laughter.

"Bet you're surprised to see me here," he commented. I acknowledged the same. "Frankly, you're the only psychologist in town that I would trust!"

Unfortunately, the payoff for setting such important limits does not always come back in such a direct manner. Children are probably the worst example, and I am resigned, with my own children, not to expect concrete results for at least the first hundred years. However, if being genuinely hated as a parent (which some experts agree is a necessary part of the process) is a prerequisite, then I have at least done my homework.

Notre Dame's Head Football Coach Lou Holtz agrees. Coach Holtz says that neither a coach nor parents are ever needed while the team/family is winning. It's when they are in trouble that unpopular decisions must be made. The Coach further comments that he has always made it a point to receive all of his necessary loving from his own family rather than his football team.

The Reciprocation of Living and Dying

The complementary relationship enjoyed by Jack Sprat and his wife, one who could eat no fat, the other no lean, is exemplary of the living/dying reciprocal. Just like Yin and Yang, closely nestled together and absolutely necessary to each others' existence, living and dying are necessary complements to the cycle of life.

As John E. Wood (2) so aptly wrote:

> In the midst of life, we are in death. In the midst of death, we are in life. None can be the divider. Who can separate life from death, or the flower from the seed, or the seed from the flower, or the ebb from the flow of the tide?
>
> The harvest contains not only its own fruit and its own death, but also the seed of harvests as yet undreamed of, its own birth.
>
> None can be a divider. What can separate the home from the love, the deed from the doer, the smile from the face, the courage from the heart, life from death?
>
> Why, then, should we fear death? In our pragmatic, down-to-earth experience, death has proved to be adventurous and fruitful. It is not without sadness that we look back upon our childhood in "the dear, dead days," but surely the ability and the promise of our adulthood outweigh the sadness.
>
> The seed splits, dies, that the sprout may come. The minutes die quickly; the hours contain greater promise. The days come and go, but the years measure our achievements.
>
> Let us distinguish, then between live death and dead death. If the minutes do not add up to an hour of achievement, there is death, tragically dead. There are dead adults walking; there are crippled shut-ins living.

Peter Drucker (3), long considered one of the nation's foremost authorities in career management, put it this way:

> The day is gone in which we restrict our work life to forty years in the same job for a gold watch. The question that we need to ask is, 'Can I be happy, healthy, creative, and productive in this job for

two years and gain valuable experience during that time?' If the answer is yes, then such experience becomes our next stepping stone.

A neighbor of mine, years ago, who had never heard of Drucker, bragged constantly about how lucky he was to have retired at age 55, a goal that would be revered by many. He had had twenty/twenty eyesight in his youth, which was now diminished to legally blind.

Walt's "career" had started at age seventeen, right out of high school, with Bulova watches in the assembly line. At a time when many were having difficulty finding or keeping a job, Walt always took care of his family well. Two years prior to retirement, Walt's wife had left him, at a time when divorce was anything but popular, for another man thirteen years her junior.

Now Walt listens to the Talking Book version of *Time* magazine each week, and can't read the face of his gold retirement watch because it's not in braille. Yet anything less than what Walt accomplished would have been seen at the time by his family as unstable, a man obviously not able to hold down a decent long-term job.

To Live Until We Say Goodbye

One of the most powerful statements ever presented about the quality of living life to the fullest is a combined effort by Elisabeth Kubler-Ross and Mal Warshaw (4). This photographic essay called, *To Live Until We Say Good-bye*, is a gripping look at the lives of several people, ages five through seventy-two, who were willing to share their very personal last days with Dr. Kubler-Ross.

One of those special persons was Louise, age fifty-seven, who was diagnosed as terminal with cancer in 1976. Over the months that followed, Louise struggled with all of the familiar questions facing persons with cancer. What are my odds — with surgery — without surgery — radiation — chemotherapy — or simply wait for the inevitable end?

But Louise made a different choice. She chose to live her life to the fullest until the end — exceeding all medical expectations for the last days of her life.

This is an excerpt from the reflections offered by Elisabeth at the memorial service for Louise on July 22, 1978:

> She has become a symbol and example of what it is like to make use of the human right *of free choice.*
>
> She not only chose to serve her church and her hospital patients, she also made the not so easy decision to accept her diagnosis of cancer and *to live with it.* She literally lived with it; she loved her body and chose not to have surgery — her survival far exceeded all medical and scientific expectation. But it is not only the quantity of time Louise had, in spite of the fact that she chose not to accept any conventional treatment; it is what she made out of this extra time that made Louise an example to all of us and the many whose lives she has touched and the hundreds of thousands she will touch in the future.
>
> *Instead of becoming bitter when she was prematurely retired,* she saw needy people and frightened patients in her home and made a blessing out of it.
>
> *Instead of going through a series of surgeries, chemotherapy or radiation,* she used her own inner, positive energy, love, and her own healing power to control the speeding of the malignancy.
>
> *Instead of becoming despondent and depressed over her inability to get around,* she fixed her home up in such a way that she was able to function to the very end and to become an inspiration to all who entered there.
>
> *Instead of allowing others to put her in a hospital or nursing home, sedated and dependent,* she signed herself out and started to paint

at home, living long enough to see her work exhibited and to share many of her paintings with those she loved (5).

Bernie Siegel (6) agrees. In his most recent book, *Peace, Love, and Healing,* Dr. Siegel discusses this same point in depth about the quality, not the duration of life. Siegel's critics most often attack his concept of healing out of their own ignorance. They question why people die if this whole business of positive attitude really makes a difference. If we have the power to heal, then why wouldn't the choice of life or death be ours as well?

The most important point of the matter, retorts Siegel, is not the length of our life, but rather the decision to fill each day with positive experiences. It is in the experiencing of life that the meaning of death is learned.

The impact of feelings experienced at the time of our impending death or that of a loved one is always equal to the amount of unfinished business unattended. Pound for pound, the scale is pushed out of balance by the weight of this spiritual matter. It is this very "work" that must be finished to face transition with peace and love.

"So live . . ."

William Cullen Bryant (6) said it all in a much simpler way in *Thanatopsis*:

So live, that when thy summons comes . . .
Thou go not like the quarry-slave at night,
. . . but, sustained, and soothed
By an unfaltering trust . . .

Actually, the entire essence of the message is captured in those first two words. *How we live life is how we face death. What we sow is what we reap.*

Gary's life had somehow always been riddled with a theme of abandonment. His parents had split when he was three, and as is often the case, his father was cast as the irresponsible heavy, his mother as the responsible victim. Two marriages later, while Gary was entering the rites of puberty at fifteen, he was sent to live with his Italian paternal grandfather ". . . so that you can see what your old man is really like."

Grandpa Vince and Gary became fast friends. Never having been allowed to spend much time with such a "bad influence," Gary was drawn by an internal magnet to this living image of his father. They fished, told stories, laughed, played, and learned to enjoy the simpler pleasures of life together.

When Gary's twenty-one-year-old cousin on his mother's side was killed in a boating accident, he barely felt the occasion. He saw his mother briefly at the funeral, had a few harsh words with her, and then returned to the safety net of his grandparents.

Gary was again jolted briefly, but seemed to absorb with ease, the auto accident which claimed the life of one of his best childhood friends. The funeral was just far enough away that Gary was relieved when Grandpa told him he would be unable to make the trip.

When Gary's only sister was killed a year later in an auto accident while returning from the beach with her boyfriend, the family quickly fell apart — except for Grandpa and Gary, who seemed to be tighter friends than ever. Gary's mother and stepfather chose separation so quickly, it was almost as if the sister had been holding the relationship together.

One month to the day of his sister's death, Gary's grandpa died in his sleep of congestive heart failure. It was Gary's suicide attempt on the day of Grandpa's funeral that brought him to a private psychiatric hospital where he was diagnosed with depression, the onset of which began with a "chemical imbalance." Gary was to remain "in treatment" another ten months (the extent of his insurance coverage), and nine months into his treatment, had not yet begun to struggle through the enormous losses that had occurred in the two years prior to his hospitalization.

For parents not to be equipped for such desperate circumstances is understandable. But when the professional community, paid for their services, are seemingly no better prepared, perhaps it's time for an investigation.

Is or About To Be?

One of the most important debates in Christian theology has yet to reach the grass roots of the local church. Somehow, in the translation of the scriptures, the admonition of Jesus that the Kingdom of God is at hand, hinges on a singular key word that scholars argue was either "Imminent," that is *about* to happen, or "immanent," that *is* happening now.

The translation is an imperative one to those who are trying to opt for "the big reward or punishment at death" or to decide that this *is* it, and our readiness to be real is of utmost importance. The argument always seemed to me to be a moot point. Assuming the *Is* version to be correct, one has all of the bases covered either way, to say nothing of the fact that keeping a clean slate from day to day is the most stress-free way to live. Yet accidental living carries with it much less responsibility.

Nanette is afraid of becoming pregnant again. When her first pregnancy was aborted without her parents' knowledge, she abstained from sexual activity briefly, until her fears subsided. She now has sex with three different "boyfriends" with no birth control being practiced. Nanette has good reason to be afraid. Nanette is twelve.

When asked about responsible birth control, she acknowledges that she has never been allowed to plan having sex as that would make her a promiscuous slut, which is somehow a worse consequence than abortion.

Nanette is not alone. Of the 178,009 births to women under 18 years of age in the United States during 1985, 128,317 (72%) were to unmarried women (8). To make matters worse, the myth still exists that "he got her pregnant."

A comic on *Saturday Night Live* said it best (paraphrased) in the absurd:

News flash. A new synthetic sperm product has been developed that will take the hit and miss out of pregnancy. This wonderful new product will be marketed under the title of "I Can't Believe This Is Really Sperm!"

The question of "Is" or "About To Be" has been an issue long before synthetic sperm or Christian theology. Youth who have never heard of either are aware, at an increasingly early age, that they have a decided hand in running or ruining their lives.

"Hot Rockin' Y106," WHLY-FM, Leesburg, Florida, plays the latest rock all day long. Recently, combining efforts with The Chrysalis Foundation, Inc., of Winter Park, Florida, a Public Service program has been aired on an experimental basis. Would youth, accustomed to listening mindlessly to the latest top 40, take time out to call in and discuss personal problems anonymously on the air — from 1:00 a.m. to 3:00 a.m. on Monday morning?

The answer is a resounding, "Yes!" With few exceptions since the onset of the program in June, 1989, all incoming lines to the station have been jammed with serious, thoughtful calls about such accidental circumstances as Nanette's. A network is not only being established on the air, but discussion of forming neighborhood support groups is already starting (9). Concerned parents, grandparents, and youth, willing to help each other, can perhaps impact the living of life by accident more than any other resource.

Summary

Playing for keeps is the existential choice of bringing our own precious marbles to the game. Real life is not a role play nor is it played with borrowed marbles.

Being responsible begins with having a philosophy about life and the living of it. That philosophy becomes reality every time a responsible stand is taken for one's convictions. Just like the blacksmith shapes the horseshoe at white heat temperatures, a belief system is forged in the willingness to take a stand and the heat that goes with it. Nothing of value was ever gained without such lessons. What appears to be accidental is only the unconscious mind testing its mettle behind the confusion of excuses.

REFERENCES

(1) Tom Shulman. Original screenplay of *Dead Poets Society*. Reviewed in *Rolling Stone*, #555, June 19, 1989, p. 29. A motion picture starring Robin Williams by Touchstone Pictures, 1989.

(2) John E. Wood. Untitled work read at The Unitarian Church, Orlando, Florida, February 27, 1972.

(3) Mary Harrington-Hall. "A Conversation with Peter Drucker" in *Psychology Today*, Vol. 1, #10, March 1968, pp. 20-25, 70-72.

(4) Elisabeth Kubler-Ross and Mal Warshaw. *To Live Until We Say Good-bye*. Englewood Cliffs, New Jersey: Prentice-Hall, Inc., 1978.

(5) Elisabeth Kubler-Ross and Mal Warshaw. *To Live Until We Say Good-bye*. Englewood Cliffs, New Jersey: Prentice-Hall, Inc., 1978, p. 109.

(6) Bernie Siegel, M.D., *Peace, Love, and Healing*. New York: Harper and Row, 1989.

(7) William Cullen Bryant. "Thanatopsis," *Poems*. New York: Appleton, 1875.

(8) Jacqueline Smollar and Theodora Ooms. *Young Unwed Fathers: A Summary Report*. Washington, D.C.: Department of Health and Human Services, 1989.

(9) Tom M. Saunders. "Bedtime Stories with Aunt Marybeth and Uncle Tom," *Growing Up in Central Florida*. Volume I, Number IV, Orlando, Florida: Kennedy-Lyon Publishing Co., September, 1989.

10

BOUNDARIES: THE SHAPE OF THINGS TO COME

Yet another traveling salesman story — only this one has a decidedly different ending.

When the traveling salesman stops at the farmer's home to inquire if there is a room for the night, the farmer apologizes and says that the only room left is that of his daughter, Katrina. However, he generously offers this room on one condition. His daughter is a virgin, and he wants her to remain such.

Katrina, provocative and given to flirting, playfully tells the salesman, as they turn in, that her father's instructions are to be heeded. In fact, she adds, "I'm putting this row of pillows in the bed between us, and you are not to cross them under any conditions."

The salesman, having given his word, agrees, and drifts off to sleep, having good dreams as he goes.

In the morning, when the salesman awakens, there is no sign of Katrina. Still reveling in his own fantasies about what might have been, he packs his suitcase and prepares to leave.

As he goes to his car, he sees Katrina in a nearby field, across the fence, milking the cow. This morning, she looks even more radiant than last evening.

"Would you mind terribly if I were to jump the fence, and

come visit with you?"

Katrina's reply came quickly. "If you couldn't make it over the pillows, you'll never make it over the fence!"

The Need for Boundaries

As cited earlier, Lenin once said that rules are like pie crusts — they are made to be broken. That axiom could not be more true than in the family system where the constant negotiation of boundaries continuously reenacts the parent/child struggle about power, authority, responsibility, and codependency.

Power

Tipp O'Neill, then Speaker of the House, once commented that power is the illusion created by standing in the middle of two mirrors and seeing images of ourselves mirrored back and forth infinitely.

The same idea was portrayed in *The Wizard of Oz* when Toto accidentally knocked over the screen hiding The Great Oz. To everyone's amazement, The Oz was a small, miserable, lonely man with a megaphone who had conned everyone into believing that he was powerful. Perhaps, in the final analysis, that's what power is — convincing another that you have something that they want.

For generations, parents have had power over their offspring because they could bear children. Men have power over women when it is a workable arrangement. The rich have power over the poor as long as the myth remains intact.

Yet, in every phase of history, there have been children, in special families, who knew how to negotiate their rights, and had the courage to do so. In every generation, there has been an Eleanor Roosevelt who quietly scoffed at male superiority and went about doing her business, even when slurred with the worst cut of all — that she was behaving just like a man! And in every revolution, when the peasants were angry enough to not take it anymore, change was forged without a budget.

Authority

If power is the edict of stated strength, then authority might be the Gold Seal which carries with it the implicit belief system that such stated strength is real and needed.

Gold, as a metal, has an inherent value based upon supply and demand. Contrived uses and its attractive color have demonstrated its economic value. Its psychological value is controlled conversely by greed and fear.

Power has an intrinsic value based upon supply and demand. Contrived needs create an assigned economic value. Authority is, then, the psychological struggle over power controlled conversely by greed and fear.

In the classic struggle between Church and State over the centuries, only Charlemagne and Napoleon dared grab the crown from the Pope's hands and place it on their own head during coronation. This act did more to set the stage for what was to come than any other feat that was later accomplished.

Responsibility

As discussed in several prior chapters, responsibility is where the rubber meets the road. All of the supply and demand, all of the myth, is hollow without action. The moment of risking responsibility for change, *to change*, is the actual proof that power and authority exist. Everything else is just fluff — for show.

Codependency

If you've bought the farm, committed to a self-sufficient existence of supplying your own needs, and physically walked and fenced the boundaries, there is only one relevant question left to answer. "Are you going to try to do it by yourself, Bucky, or are you going to share the experience?"

John Donne said it best with "Never send to see for whom the bell tolls . . . it tolls for thee." There are periods of time when "island" behavior is not only acceptable, but sought and preferred. While abbeys and monasteries have never flourished, they have always served a temporary function for the interim when alone looked better than being hurt again.

Sooner or later, just as though we were all connected by those same giant rubber bands discussed earlier, we are pulled back by the gravity of the system, and the struggle for healthy codependency commences all over again.

During the Ming Dynasty in China at the turn of the 17th century, carvings of the seated bodhisattvas flourished. The bodhisattva was an ideal of Mahayana Buddhism.

It is a being with all of the attributes of a Buddha, but who, due to compassion for other sentient beings, postpones *nirvana* until all are saved. They are asexual beings since the realm of sexual desire has little application to their transcendental state (1).

The critical question still must be raised about how much compassion, how long? Like the old definition in Al-Anon of a slip: To feel a moment of compassion.

The Nature of Boundaries

As with many related issues, the one of boundaries is paradoxical in nature. Boundaries provide structure, a framework within which responsible decision-making can be accomplished.

In the role of parent, a rule is established about crossing streets. With months of prior training, rules about traffic lights reviewed, dangers of cars and trucks killing the innocent graphically described, the moment now comes when the parent must open their palms and bet that their parenting has worked — against life or death!

While rules are generally made to err on the conservative side, they are usually established for the benefit of the child — at least until the child approaches puberty and becomes the feared rebel. At that point, parents typically construct a rule system that protects parents from themselves and their own incestuous fears.

Bobby was fourteen. If the helping professional's diagnostic bible had assigned a code number for age fourteen, it would have been the only diagnosis necessary.

Bobby had just flunked out of school, but was too stoned to notice. When asked if he thought that he had a drug problem, he stated emphatically, "No, I'm not using any more than my friends." (The old P. U. test — peer urinalysis.)

As is often the profile, Bobby had been a wonderfully compliant child until age eleven. It was, as if, overnight he became belligerent, uncontrollable, and defiant to any rules or structure. As is also often the case, Bobby was extremely bright and spontaneous — a threat to any power base. It was Bobby who had identified age eleven as the turning point.

"Bobby, what exactly do you think happened at age eleven?"

"I don't really know. It seemed like our family quit having fun together. I have a younger brother and sister. The most fun that we would have was when we all played in the bathtub together. That stopped when I was eleven. My mom and dad also stopped hugging me and kissing me good night."

"That's a lot of change for one year," I observed stoically. "What do you think happened?"

Without a second thought, Bobby replied, "I guess the tub got too small."

What a classically simple story about the rites of puberty and the subtle shift in power/authority/responsibility that begins to evolve in the family system. Not all of the stories can be so easily reduced to such a simple analysis, that your life goes down the drain when the tub gets too small and your parents quit hugging you.

An Historic National Model

In every culture, regardless of economic base, power, authority, and the responsibility needed to maintain them, control is maintained by 2% of the population.

My earliest recollection of television was watching the McCarthy hearings. Pinko Communism was to be feared, and its people were dominated by a mindless self-servient dictatorship. I am ashamed to admit that I was in graduate school before I learned from a professor who had visited the Soviet Union that Russia was only one state within the Soviet Union and that only 2% of their population control is under a Communist regime that is not respected by the mass.

I immediately breathed a sigh of relief that *I* lived in a democracy where everyone has a say. Yet, when is the last time that you can remember a poor person with a set of ideals so strong, so untarnished, that the individual could be elected as President of the United States without selling out? Lincoln, perhaps?

And does anyone remember an American *woman* president? Our liberal democracy cannot even rise to a straw vote yet that women should even have rights.*

H. Richard Niebuhr (2) distinguishes between ethic as what we believe, and moral as what we do. So the truths that we all agree are "self-evident" are really forged daily in the reality of "what is."

Editorial Note: For all of you "snot-nosed critics" (as a minister friend always referred to them), I was born in America by chance, but I live here by choice. Of all of the systems that I have yet been privileged to observe from the inside, I have found nothing that would compare to the freedom or responsibility that we have available as citizens of the United States. That in no way signifies that the system is above reproach or improvement.

Toward Developing A Family Model

The same is true of families. There is no democracy in families — only an illusion of one.

Every biological family commences with two people of different political persuasions — not a form of government — but a set of ethics about how a family system should ultimately operate. Each of these two persons are backed by their respective clans as if connected by a giant tug-of-war rope. Kids are the booty over which the war is waged and are often sacrificed to "save them."

Steve's biological parents have been divorced for seven years. Steve is fourteen. At least once each year since the divorce, a family meeting has been called by Steve or one of his two siblings (formerly three siblings). The meetings have been held in jail, the hospital, a funeral home, and in the juvenile detention center.

This year, Steve is before the same judge who ordered him last year to a private school because he was doing drugs. He now does more sophisticated drugs and has added homosexual experience to his repertoire. Confirming his own worst fears (Dad said that the reason he left Mom was about an affair, explicit details discussed, that she had had with her best girl friend), Steve is then told by Dad that " . . . he has turned out just like his mom."

Steve is next ordered, by the Court, to a more expensive, exclusive private school. In spite of detailed information provided to the judge about why the family continues to meet as a product of the unfinished anger between the two clans, the judge unwittingly becomes a part of the family politics and assigns the financial burden to Dad because he supposedly has the best earning power. Once again, the primary system of power and authority has only become a mirror of the confused family system.

The development of a family model must commence with understanding the politics of the ancestral clans. Where the ethic and moral are in unison, there is no inconsistency. Many models of family life, running the gamut of extremes, work because they are consistent between the ethic and the moral. Where parents espouse one set of standards and live a second, a chasm known as The Achilles Heel develops.

How offspring come to know about The Heel is worth another manuscript. One fantasy of mine is that somewhere, shortly after conception, kids begin taking notes about which behaviors and feelings make which parent twitch. Inevitably, they stumble across a group of behaviors and feelings that make both parents' knees jerk, hence the finding of The Heel.

Where The Heel is enshrouded in family secrets, the vulnerability increases in direct proportion. This extra leverage will typically become worth its weight in gold as the offspring approach puberty, and the stakes of extortion reach their maximum limits.

Imagine, as John Lennon once said, something different. As there are no families without inconsistencies of some kind between the ethic and the moral, then a reasonable place to commence would be to become as familiar as possible, as parents, with these discrepancies. Once aware, change might be considered, or simply an agreement that these differences exist and are to be left intact.

Imagine a family discussion when you were growing up in which parents admitted to you that the weekly mandatory sermon in church *was* boring and irrelevant and that most spiritual experiences never occur inside the walls of a church?

Imagine two parents, holding you in love, while explaining their own personal anger and inadequate feelings which you happen to be mirroring at the time, rather than the usual boring parent lecture that was given instead?

How absurd to even imagine! Such disclosure, as any good parent or government leader would quickly tell you, not only seriously erodes your power base, but diminishes authority which will, in turn, make you both weak and vulnerable for attack from the outside. Most parents would find it unthinkable to be aware of their own sexual fears, much less express them to their children, or worse yet, *about* their children!

Yet, it is in this moment of vulnerability that change occurs — the risk of the *Is* that dismantles the time bomb of children locating The Heel and turning it to their own advantage. When both clans have been honest with their own offspring, and then further extended that honesty to the clan of the intended Other whom they have pledged to marry, a major step toward harmony in families, and simultaneously toward world peace, will have occurred.

When Marley escorts Scrooge to see Christmas Future in the Charles Dicken's classic, *A Christmas Carol*, it is the last in a series of humbling experiences that brings Scrooge to his knees. Knowing that the Past and the Present, unaltered, become the Future, the decision is a clear one.

Portable Boundaries and <u>Co</u> Dependency

Taking the given that boundaries are structure, a framework within which to make smaller important decisions more comfortably, then it would hold true that the more portable and flexible those boundaries are, the more anxious all participants become who are involved.

If Mexico or Canada were to mark their geographical boundaries with bright red rubber pylons, consider the difficulty which the two countries would have remaining friends? Consider further, the President and Vice President of the United States, disagreeing among themselves over not only the placement of the pylons but their respective color codes?

When parents are confused or act confused (probably no noticeable distinction) about boundaries, coming from their own Heel posture, children will always find a way to force their hand or their Heel. Until those major issues are settled, the children cannot effectively leave home nor can the parents plan a life of their own that does not include the kids.

A couple in their nineties arrive for their first "marriage counseling" session, and the wife announces up front that she only wants a divorce — that sixty-seven of the last sixty-eight years have been pure hell.

"Well, if you don't mind my asking," inquired the counselor, ". . . why have you waited until now to divorce?"

Came the reply, "We had to wait until all of the kids were dead!"

What often masks as "finding one's self" or "middle age crisis" is, at a much different level, a struggle centered around the "death" of the last child about to leave home. Often commencing as early as the onset of puberty of that child, both parents are sent scrambling for an identity outside of marriage and children that inadvertently results in the accidental "death" of both.

Most unlike the adolescent described earlier who rebels against the horrible structure of home by joining the Marines, a parent will bolt by finding "security" with another person who reeks even stronger of codependency needs than the family from which they are fleeing. Hence, the expression, out of the frying pan into the fire.

A Revisit To Chaos

If chaos were redefined simply as a time of change and all of the uncertainties commonly attached, it would perhaps not be so frightening.

Change is healthy. Change is necessary. Change always involves dying and being reborn.

Fritz Perls (3), considered by himself to be the "finder" of gestalt therapy, scrawled in his own handwriting, as an introduction to his classic work, *Gestalt Therapy Verbatim*, "To suffer one's death and be reborn is not easy."

Death means letting go of, moving to the cutting edge, and trying out new wings that would have never worked for the caterpillar. Reborn is to synthesize all of our experiences to date that will allow the evolution of the soul to move to a different plane.

Writing about history will always be more comfortable than making history. Reading about history is far enough removed from the battle line as to not even hear the sound of history being made.

I was told recently of a woman who contained her anxiety for more than a decade by reading voraciously everything that she could check out from the local library. When she was finished with her last book, she went to her bedroom and blew out her brains — along with all of the wonderful knowledge that they contained.

Summary

Boundaries are necessary for living, for changing, for dying, and for evolving to the next stage of growth.

The choice is a simple one. We can either forge those boundaries out of our own experience, engage others in a healthy dialogue of codependency, or else force others to provide them for us by acting as if we don't know how. The advantage of "not knowing" is an addictive kind of codependency which will always insure that our family, biological and psychosocial, will take care of us.

Our family, or someone else's family, acting out of their own sense of desperation, will continue to take care of us for as long as they can be duped into "saving our life" instead of killing us.

REFERENCES

(1)   Exhibit, The Appleton Museum of Art, Ocala, Florida, 1989.

(2)   H. Richard Niebuhr. *Faith and Ethics: The Theology of H. Richard Niebuhr.* Edited by Paul Ramsey. New York: Harper and Row, 1965.

(3)   Fritz Perls. *Gestalt Therapy Verbatim.* Moab, UT: Real People Press, 1959.

APPENDIX A

THE LIFE CHANGES SCALE

Please make one copy of this scale for each member of your family age ten or older to complete. Each question means exactly what each family member perceives it to mean.

Write three answers in the space provided for each question.

In the blank, to the left of each answer, write the number of the year that you would most associate with each answer.

When you have completed each answer with an associated year, follow the instructions at the end for charting your answers.

Name your three most intimate friends.

_____ 1)

_____ 2)

_____ 3)

Name your three most passionate enemies.

_____ 4)

_____ 5)

_____ 6)

Name your three most important personal
issues under the category of "unfinished
business".

_____   7)

_____   8)

_____   9)

Name your three illnesses of choice (What are
your "target organs"? To what does your body
usually succumb?)

_____   10)

_____   11)

_____   12)

Name your three most memorable accidents.

_____   13)

_____   14)

_____   15)

Name your three greatest losses.

_____   16)

_____   17)

_____   18)

Name your three most significant geographical moves.

_____   19)

_____   20)

_____   21)

Name your three greatest fears.

——————— 22)

——————— 23)

——————— 24)

Name your three favorite forms of dependency.

——————— 25)

——————— 26)

——————— 27)

Name your three best defenses (major life excuses used most often to avoid responsibility.

——————— 28)

——————— 29)

——————— 30)

INSTRUCTIONS FOR CHARTING:

Draw a scale using the model below as an example.

On the left end of the scale, print "BIRTH" and write your Month, Day, and Year of Birth.

On the right end of the scale, print "PRESENT" and write today's Month, Day, and Year.

Take each item # from the questionnaire and place it on the scale. Use the Year which you assigned to each item # as a way of locating its relative position on the scale.

See the example below:

          Name your three most intimate friends.

__1956__   1) Rhonda

__1947__   2) Christine

__1964__   3) Garry

          Name your three most passionate enemies.

__1984__   4) Marge

Month & Day of Birth   Today's Month & Day

February 20, 1942

_____   _____

	#1	#2	#3	#4	
BIRTH | . . . . |					**PRESENT**
	1	1	1	1	
	9	9	9	9	
Year of Birth	5	4	6	8	Today's Year
	6	7	4	4	
__1942__					_____

APPENDIX B

FAMILY RE-UNION RULES

The following conditions need to be discussed and endorsed by your family prior to scheduling an extended family re-union:

1) Two consultants will work together with the family throughout the period contracted. The fee for an eight-hour day is $3600. Any time beyond that period is $425 per hour. The family shall agree by consensus when to stop. All day sessions are generally scheduled from 8:30 a.m. to 4:30 p.m. Any other expenses associated with scheduling a re-union such as travel expenses incurred by family members and/or consultants will also be the family's responsibility and will be shared by *all* family members as discussed below.

2) All expenses are shared by all family members fourteen years of age and older. Agreement about how these expenses are shared is part of the family process needed to indicate a willingness of the family to work together. A "quarterback" needs to be selected in the family to help coordinate this process as well as to schedule the re-union.

3) Since an exceptional amount of professional time is being committed, the session must be paid in full by **cashier's check** in U.S. currency to Tom M. Saunders, Ph.D., **as soon as possible but *at least two weeks prior*** to the scheduled date. Cancellation needs to occur prior to that

two-week deadline as fees will not be refunded within two weeks before the scheduled date. Fees will also not be refunded should designated *key members* decide not to show, or leave before the session has ended. *Key members* will be identified and listed on the back of this contract before the contract is signed.

4) Each member participating must sign a copy of these rules that will also serve as a release to the consultants acknowledging that key members understand that the sessions will be video/audio taped for the family's own use and benefit. These signed agreements must be submitted at the time payment is made for the session. At that same time, blank tapes also need to be supplied by the family. Four VHS tapes or three Beta will be required.

5) It is the request of the consultants that family members leave during the session for bathroom breaks **only.** If you must leave to smoke, please become aware of the process happening within the family at the moment you need to leave, talk with the family about your need to leave, and keep the leave brief. No smoking within the building please.

No alcohol or other mood altering drugs may be used during the session including caffeine and sugar.

Eating will be limited to a designated meal period agreed upon by the family with the exception of special diets such as with diabetes. Family members will be responsible for bringing their own food as the session will continue through the meal. The consultants will provide for their own needs. Nutritious food is strongly suggested.

Please discuss any further questions with the co-consultants.

Please sign and date on the back after reaching consensus with the consultants as to who the key members of your family are.

BIBLIOGRAPHY

Alger, Ian. "Audio-visual Techniques in Family Therapy," *Techniques in Family Therapy: A Primer*, ed. Donald Bloch. New York: Grune and Stratton, 1973.

Bach, Richard. *Illusions*. New York: Random House, 1977.

Baker, David, Th.B., D.O. From a lecture about the nature of herpes viruses. Philadelphia, Pennsylvania, December 13, 1987.

Brooks, Mel, Norman Steinberg, Andrew Bergman, Richard Pryor, and Alan Uger. *Blazing Saddles*. A motion picture written and directed for Warner Brothers by Mel Brooks, 1974.

Bryant, William Cullen. "Thanatopsis," *Poems*. New York: Appleton, 1875.

Exhibit. The Appleton Museum of Art, Ocala, Florida, 1989.

Frost, Robert. "Mending Wall," *Modern Verse in English: 1900 — 1950*, ed. David Cecil and Allen Tate. New York: Macmillan, 1958.

Hall, Mary Harrington. "A Conversation with Peter Drucker" in *Psychology Today*, Vol. I, No. 10, March, 1968, pp. 20-25, 70-72.

————. "A Conversation with Viktor Frankl," *Psychology Today*, Vol. I, No. 9, February, 1968, pp. 56-63.

Hammerschlag, Carl A. *The Dancing Healers*. San Francisco: Harper and Row, 1988.

Holtz, Lou. "A letter to the Next Generation." *Time*, April 10, 1989.

_____. A personal interview with the Board of Directors, The Chrysalis Foundation, Inc., at The Hyatt Grand Cypress Hotel, Lake Buena Vista, Florida, May 24, 1989.

Jung, Carl. "The Concept of the Collective Unconscious." *Archetypes and the Collective Unconscious, Collected Works*, ed. R. F. Hull. Princeton, New Jersey: University Press, 1928.

Kempler, Walter. *Experiential Psychotherapy within Families*. New York: Brunner/Mazel, 1981.

Kopp, Sheldon. *If You See the Buddha on the Road, Kill Him!* New York: Dell Books, 1969.

Kubler-Ross, Elisabeth. Presentation during a five-day seminar in Oviedo, Florida, on death and dying, 1983.

_____ and Mal Warshaw. *To Live until We Say Good-Bye*. Englewood Cliffs, New Jersey: Prentice Hall, Inc. 1978, p. 109.

Langsley, D. G. and D. M. Kaplan. *The Treatment of Families in Crisis*. New York: Grune and Stratton, 1968.

Lawick-Goodall, Jane. *My Friends, The Wild Chimpanzees*. Washington, D.C.: National Geographic Society, 1967.

Lennon, John and Paul McCartney. "The End." *Abbey Road*, Hollywood, California: Capitol Records, Inc., 1969.

May, Rollo. *The Courage To Create*. New York: W. W. Norton, 1975.

Montague, Ashley. *Touching: The Human Significance of Skin*. New York: Columbia University Press, 1971.

Muller, W. J., III, M. D. *Journal of Hospital and Community Psychiatry*, Vol. 25:9, 1974, pp. 587-590.

Niebuhr, H. Richard. *Faith and Ethics: The Theology of H. Richard Niebuhr*, ed. Paul Ramsey. New York: Harper and Row, 1965.

Perls, Fritz. *Gestalt Therapy Verbatim*. Moab Utah: Real People Press, 1959.

Satir, Virginia. "Therapeutic Use of the Self in Relation To Family

Healing." A conference held at the First Presbyterian Church in Maitland, Florida, November 14, 1987.

Saunders, Tom. "Bedtime Stories with Aunt Marybeth and Uncle Tom," *Growing Up in Central Florida*. Vol. I, No. IV, Orlando, Florida: Kennedy-Lyon Publishing Co., September, 1989.

Shulman, Tom. Original screenplay of *Dead Poets Society*, reviewed *Rolling Stone*, No. 555, June 19, 1989, p. 29. A motion picture starring Robin Williams by Touchstone Pictures, 1989.

Siegel, Bernie, M.D. *Love, Medicine, and Miracles*. New York: Harper and Row, 1986.

————. *Peace, Love, and Healing*. New York: Harper and Row, 1989.

Smollar, Jacqueline, and Theodora Ooms. *Young Unwed Fathers: A Summary Report*. Washington, D.C.: Department of Health and Human Services, 1989.

Szasz, Thomas S. "Justifying Coercion Through Theology and Therapy." An address delivered at The Evolution of Psychotherapy, December 13, 1986.

Taub-Bynum, E. Bruce. *The Family Unconscious*. Wheaton, Illinois: Theosophical Press, 1984.

The Book. Wheaton, Illinois: Tyndale House Publishers, Inc., 1984.

Thurber, James. *Further Fables for Our Time*. New York: Simon and Schuster, 1956.

Tillich, Paul. *The Courage To Be*. New Haven, Connecticut: Yale University Press, 1959.

Whitaker, Carl. A multiple families group experience in St. Maarten, The French Antilles, March 1986.

Wood, John E. An untitled work read at The Unitarian Church, Orlando, Florida, February 27, 1972.

INDEX

-A-

-B-

-D-

-E-

-F-

-S-

-T-

-U-

-V-

-W-

-Y-

ABOUT THE AUTHOR

Born in rural Ohio, Tom Saunders was the fifth generation to live on the same street — in a village with only three streets and a population of 100! Learning as a youngster about his extended family and the nurturing strength of community, he has continued to prod existing schools of psychotherapy about what seems quite obvious — working with the family system as a whole.

Muriel Whitaker said it best when asked, "Why is family work so important to Carl and you?" Muriel replied simply, "I guess because we all come from a family."

From those early beginnings, Tom's best training as a counseling psychologist has come from his own family and the extended families with whom he has surrounded himself. His work has been profoundly influenced by the Cherokee Indians-Eastern Band, extensive travels and dialogue with European families, and the numerous families with whom he has consulted over the last twenty years. Two years of graduate studies in theology have also had a marked influence on his spiritual beliefs.

Where formal training has left much to be desired, Tom has sought out the masters of family therapy and learned by their sides. He is deeply committed to the present development of a training program that will involve the best of experts from around the world in a "hands on" environment. At this proposed Central Florida campus, every aspect of family life will be presented, from a birthing center, and a day care center operated by grandparents, to a hospice-like facility.

Tom is in private practice with Family Systems Consultants in Winter Park, Florida. He works extensively with family and corporate systems, and specializes in family re-unions — a marathon meeting of the entire extended family network. Tom is the founder of The Chrysalis Foundation, Inc., which does education, research, and training with family systems nationally.